Important Instruction

Students, Parents, and Teachers can use the URL or QR code provided below to access hundreds of additional practice questions, educational videos, worksheets, mobile apps, standards information and more.

URL	QR Code
Visit the URL below and place the book access code **http://www.lumoslearning.com/a/tedbooks** **Access Code: G2ELSM-50419-P**	

Lumos Skills Mastery tedBook - 2nd Grade English Language Arts: Standards-based ELA practice workbook

Contributing Author - **Bonnie McRae**
Executive Producer - **Mukunda Krishnaswamy**
Program Director - **Priya L**
Database Administrator - **R. Raghavendra Rao**
Designer and Illustrator - **Devraj D**

First Edition - 2020

ISBN-10: 1-946795-99-2

ISBN-13: 978-1-946795-99-1

Printed in the United States of America

For permissions and additional information contact us

Lumos Information Services, LLC
PO Box 1575, Piscataway, NJ 08855-1575
http://www.LumosLearning.com

Email: support@lumoslearning.com
Tel: (732) 384-0146
Fax: (866) 283-6471

Table of Contents

Online Program Benefits

Students*

- Rigorous Standards Practice
- Technology-enhanced item types practice
- Additional learning resources such as videos and apps

Parents*

- You can review your student's online work by logging into your parent account.
- Pinpoint student areas of difficulty
- Develop custom lessons & assignments
- Access to High-Quality Question Bank

Teachers*

- Review the online work of your students
- Get insightful student reports
- Discover standards aligned videos, apps and books through EdSearch
- Easily access standards information along with the Coherence Map
- Create and share information about your classroom or school events

* Terms and Conditions apply

URL	QR Code
Visit the URL below and place the book access code **http://www.lumoslearning.com/a/tedbooks** **Access Code: G2ELSM-50419-P**	

Start using the online resources included with this book today!

Introduction

This book is designed to provide rigorous standards-aligned skills practice to second grade students. Students will obtain a better understanding of each standard and improve on their weaknesses by practicing the questions provided in this workbook. The lessons contain rigorous questions aligned to the state standards and substandards. Taking the time to work through the activities will afford students the ability to become proficient in each grade level standard.

Unlike a traditional book, this Lumos tedBook offers online access to additional learning resources and more practice questions. Practicing the questions provided in these digital workbooks will not only help students get a comprehensive review of standards, but also become familiar with the technology enhanced question types.

Why Practice by Standard?

Each standard and substandard has its own specific learning objectives. Taking the time to study and practice each standard individually will create opportunities for students to master those learning objectives and demonstrate proficiency. Additionally, students have individual strengths and weaknesses. Being able to practice content by standard allows them to efficiently strengthen areas of their weaknesses.

How Can the Lumos Study Program Prepare Students for Standardized Tests?

Student's mastery of the State Standards are being assessed using standardized testing methods. At Lumos Learning, we believe that yearlong learning and adequate practice before the actual test are the keys to success on these standardized tests. We have designed this book to help students learn each standard through engaging videos and other resources and practice using questions provided in the book and online.

What is Lumos tedBook™?

Lumos tedBook™ connects practice questions provided in this printed workbook with engaging online resources. These additional resources can be accessed using a number of devices including Android phones, iPhones, tablets and personal computers. Each Online Workbook will have some of the same questions seen in this printed book, along with additional questions, apps and videos. Students will get instant feedback and can review their answers anytime. Each student's answers and progress can be reviewed by parents and educators to reinforce the learning experience.

Discover Engaging and Relevant Learning Resources

Lumos EdSearch is a safe search engine specifically designed for teachers and students. Using EdSearch, you can easily find thousands of standards-aligned learning resources such as questions, videos, lessons, worksheets and apps. Teachers can use EdSearch to create custom resource kits to perfectly match their lesson objective and assign them to one or more students in their classroom.

To access the EdSearch tool, use the search box after you log into Lumos StepUp or use the link provided below.

http://www.lumoslearning.com/a/edsearchb	

The Lumos Standards Coherence map provides information about previous level, next level and related standards. It helps educators and students visually explore learning standards. It's an effective tool to help students progress through the learning objectives. Teachers can use this tool to develop their own pacing charts and lesson plans. Educators can also use the coherence map to get deep insights into why a student is struggling in a specific learning objective.

Teachers can access the Coherence maps after logging into the StepUp Teacher Portal or use the link provided below.

http://www.lumoslearning.com/a/coherence-map	

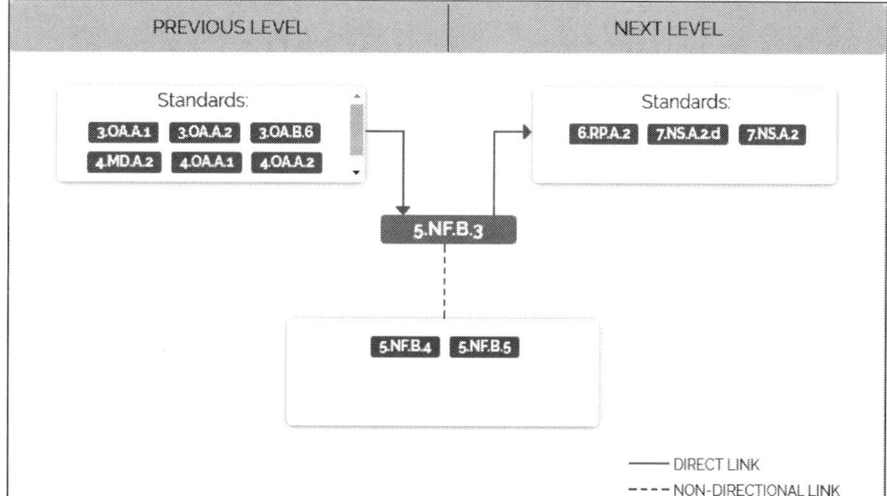

How to use this book effectively

The Lumos Program is a flexible learning tool. It can be adapted to suit a student's skill level and the time available to practice before standardized tests. Here are some tips to help you use this book and the online resources effectively:

Students

- The standards in each book can be practiced in the order designed, or in the order you prefer.
- Complete all questions in each workbook.
- Use the Online workbooks to further practice your areas of difficulty and as a way to complement classroom learning.
- Download the Lumos StepUp® app using the instructions provided in Lumos StepUp® Mobile App FAQ For Students to have access to Online resources anywhere you go.

Parents

- Help your child use Lumos StepUp® Online Workbooks by following the instructions in "Access Online Program" section.
- You can review your student's online work by login to your parent account.
- You can also conveniently access student progress report on your mobile devices by downloading the Lumos StepUp app. Please follow directions provided in "How can I Download the App?" section in Lumos StepUp® Mobile App FAQ For Parents and Teachers

Chapter 1 - Reading: Literature

The objective of the Reading Literature standards is to ensure that the student is able to read and comprehend literature (which includes stories, drama and poetry) related to Grade 2.

To help students master the necessary skills, information to help the student understand the concepts related to the standard is given. Along with this, we encourage the student to go through the resources available online on EdSearch to gain an in-depth understanding of these concepts. The EdSearch page for each lesson can be accessed with the help of the url or the QR code provided.

A small map is provided after each passage or text in which the student can enter the details as understood from the literary text. Doing this will help the student to refer to key points that help in answering the questions with ease.

Chapter 1

Lesson 1: The Question Session

In order to be able to answer questions from any story, it would be good to understand the various elements of the story. This will help you look for the answers in the story with ease.

To answer questions we need to know Who, What, Where, When, and Why. The elements of a story help you to answer these questions.

The Elements (Parts) Of a Story

1. Theme and Plot: **What**

Theme is the main idea of a story.
The plot is the most important actions, plans or events taking place in a story that support the main idea or theme of the story. There can be more than one plot in a story, and there can be one or more secondary (less important) plots (also called subplots).

2. Character(s): **Who**

The actions and thoughts and emotions of the main (major) character(s) have the most influence, are the most important, to the plot. There may be other less important characters (known as minor or secondary characters) in the story, but they will have less influence on the plot.

3. Setting(s): **Where and When**

The setting(s) for a story are the location(s) and/or time period(s) at or in which the story takes place. There can be more than one setting and more than one time period in the same story.

4. Supporting details: **Why**

The answer to "Why" is given as supporting details to the main plot or theme of the story in the text or passage.

Name: ______________________ Date: ______________

You can scan the QR code given below or use the url to access additional EdSearch resources including videos and mobile apps related to *Supporting Statements*.

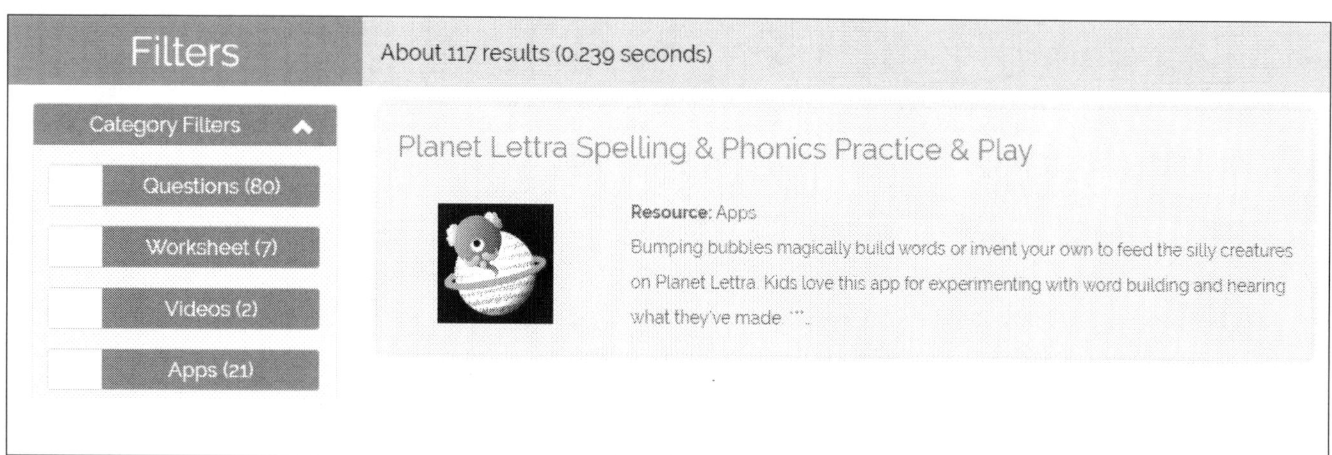

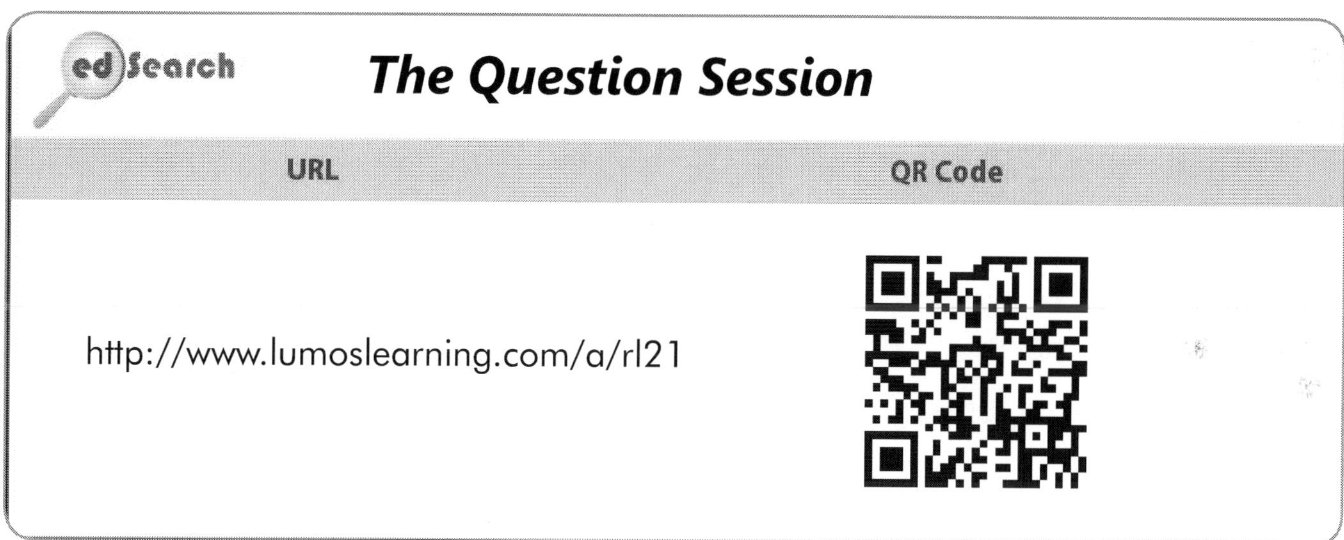

Name: ______________________ Date: ______________ 

Sara Takes a Trip

One day, Sara's dad said they were going on a trip to the beach. Sara was happy! She got her things to go. First, she found her bathing suit. She put it on. Then, she went to the bathroom and picked out her best beach towel. Sara put it in her beach bag along with her sunscreen. Her mother told her to hurry up, dad was ready. She didn't want to forget her sand shovel and tools to make a sand castle. She quickly added them to her bag. Sara hurried when she heard her dad start the van.

It was a long drive to the beach. Dad played music on the radio. Mom sang along. Skip, their dog, even whined with the songs. Sara was smiling and having fun. At last, they were there. Dad said to help unload their van. Sara carefully took the picnic basket to the table that her Mom had found by the sand dunes.

It was so nice and warm at the beach. Skip ran to the water and jumped in. Dad, Mom and Sara laughed. Mom and Sara got in the water, too. The waves felt funny hitting Sara. She and Mom smiled. Dad was fishing close by.

After a bit, Mom said they needed to stop to eat lunch. They ate hot dogs and chips. Skip ate one, too. Then, they rested.

Next, Sara and Dad made a sand castle. Skip laid down on it. That did not stop the fun.

Dad said they could all go in one more time. Even Skip joined them. They jumped and swam in the ocean water for a long time. It was getting near dark. They had to leave to go home. Sara and Skip fell asleep on the way back. Everyone had a wonderful time at the beach!

1. Who went to the beach? Mark the correct answer.

Ⓐ Sara went to the beach with her parents.
Ⓑ Sara took her dog, Skip, on a trip to the beach.
Ⓒ Sara went to the beach with friends, Amy and Joan.
Ⓓ Sara, her parents and their dog, Skip, went to the beach.

2. Mark what Sara took to the beach in her bag. Mark all that are correct.

Ⓐ Dog leash
Ⓑ Sunscreen
Ⓒ Sand shovel and tools
Ⓓ Bathing suit
Ⓔ Shells
Ⓕ Purse
Ⓖ Beach Towel

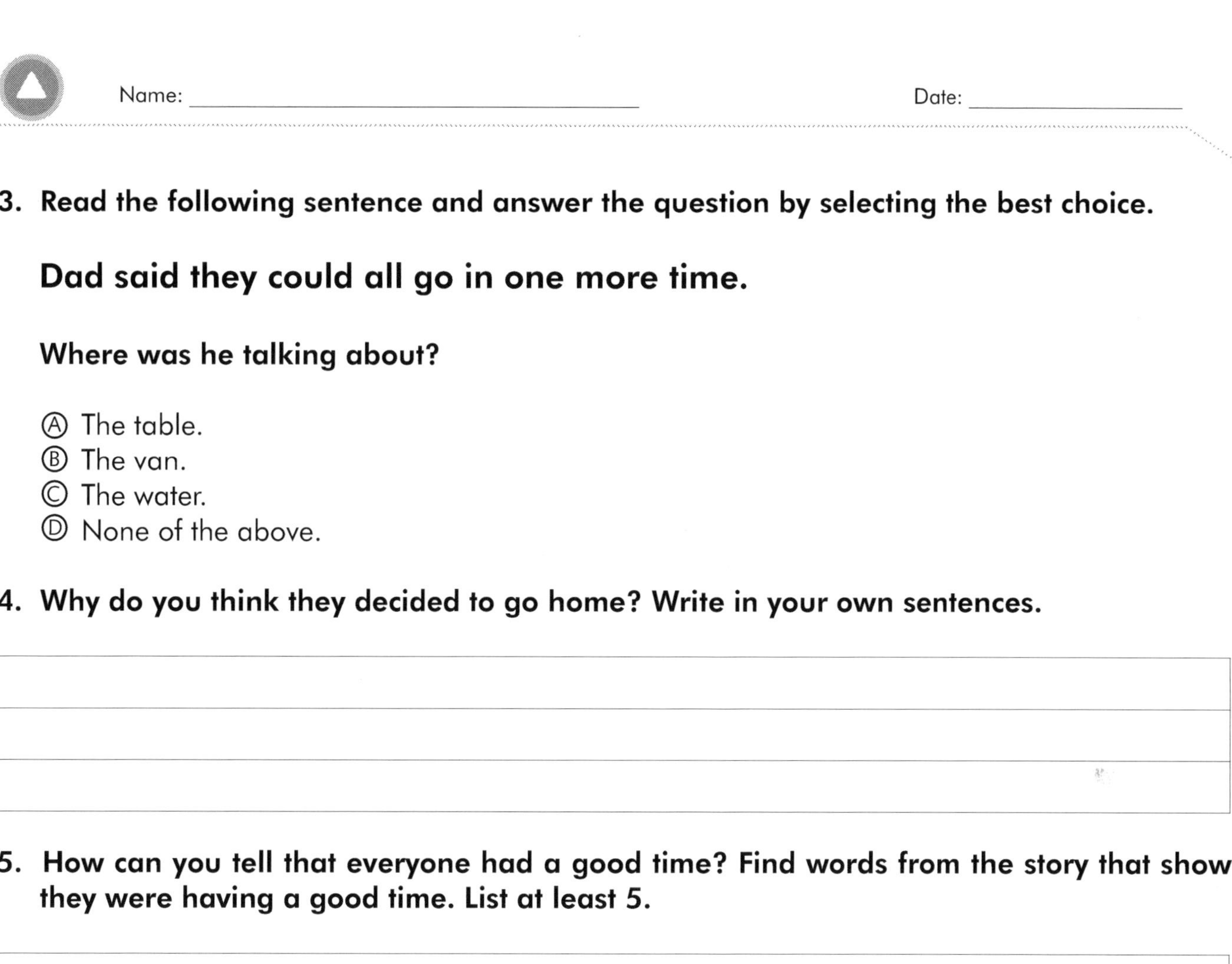

3. **Read the following sentence and answer the question by selecting the best choice.**

Dad said they could all go in one more time.

Where was he talking about?

Ⓐ The table.
Ⓑ The van.
Ⓒ The water.
Ⓓ None of the above.

4. **Why do you think they decided to go home? Write in your own sentences.**

5. **How can you tell that everyone had a good time? Find words from the story that show they were having a good time. List at least 5.**

Ramona, Betsy, and Paco

Ramona and her best friend, Betsy, loved to go outside and play when the weather was nice. They were a little worried because the wind was blowing, and it looked like rain today. Betsy had her sister bring her over to Ramona's house to see if she wanted to go outside anyway. Ramona's mother said they had to stay inside.

The girls were not happy. What could they do? They did not like to play games inside. They watched a few cartoons but were soon bored.

Next, Ramona's mother brought out coloring books, crayons, and markers. The girls colored a few pages with markers, but got tired of that, too.

Betsy said she was hungry, so they had a snack in the kitchen. In the kitchen, Betsy saw a cage. It had a large bird in it. She asked Ramona about the bird.

Ramona told her that was Paco, her parrot. Soon Ramona started talking to Paco. She said, "Paco's a pretty bird." To Betsy's surprise, Paco said, "Paco's a pretty bird." Betsy's mouth dropped open in surprise. She laughed. Then Paco laughed. Betsy asked Ramona how that happened. Ramona's mother explained it to her. "The parrot can repeat some words you say. You have to say the same thing over 45 times before he can say it back to you."

Ramona's mother told Betsy all the words Paco knew how to say. The girls had so much fun saying things to Paco and having him repeat them. He could repeat more words like, "Good morning, Paco. Hello. What? I love you, Paco." He could even whistle! Then, Ramona took Paco out of his cage. She carefully opened the cage door and out he came. He flew around the house. The girls giggled when Ramona's mother put her arm out and Paco landed on it. Then she waved her arm and off he went again. Flying and squawking. Betsy said, "This is the best time ever!" They even got to stretch out their arms and have Paco land on them. The day went by quickly. Betsy told Ramona, "Now we know what to do when we can't go outside!"

6. What did Ramona and Betsy like to do? Mark the best answer.

Ⓐ They liked to go shopping at the mall.
Ⓑ The girls loved to play outside.
Ⓒ The girls liked to play video games.
Ⓓ The girls liked to cook in the kitchen with Ramona's mother.

7. **Complete the sentence with what happened. Use the story to help you.**

Today, the girls could not go outside because

8. **What did the girls do instead of playing outside?**

Mark all that are correct.

Ⓐ They cleaned house for Ramona's mother.
Ⓑ They played with Paco, the parrot.
Ⓒ They had a snack in the kitchen.
Ⓓ They watched cartoons.
Ⓔ They colored with markers.

9. **How did the girls feel after Ramona's mother said they could not play outside? Pick the best sentence from the story.**

Ⓐ Ramona's mother said they had to stay inside.
Ⓑ The girls were not happy.
Ⓒ It had a large bird in it.
Ⓓ She laughed.

10. **Details tell "what" about a story.**

Put an x on the right box or boxes that explains the sentences below.

	Yes	No
Ramona and Betsy are friends		
The weather was good.		
Paco is a hummingbird		
The girls had fun with Paco.		

Chapter 1

Lesson 2: Recount stories

Recount stories, including fables and folktales from diverse cultures, and determine their central message, lesson, or moral.

You can scan the QR code given below or use the url to access additional EdSearch resources including videos and mobile apps related to Recount stories.

Recount stories

URL	QR Code
http://www.lumoslearning.com/a/rl22	

Name: ____________________ Date: ____________

An adaptation of The Rose Princess

A long time ago, in a faraway kingdom, there lived a beautiful princess. The princess had long red hair. She loved red roses. They called her Princess Rose.

At night-time, she would go out on her balcony. A gold bird would fly to her and sing. She would sing with the bird. The whole village would fall asleep and dream good thoughts.

There was an evil witch who did not like the princess. She cast a spell to turn the princess' hair black.

The next night when the gold bird came and sang, the princess sang again. This time, the village people went to sleep but had bad dreams.

The princess did not know what to do.

She asked the golden bird for help. The bird told her to dip her hair in rose water. The princess did, and it worked.

This made the witch even angrier. She cast a second spell.

This time she got rid of all the roses in the kingdom.

The princess asked the gold bird for help. The bird told her the same thing. The princess could not find any roses.

Just then a prince came with a lock of the princess' hair and dropped it on the ground. It grew a rose bush full of roses. The princess had rose petals to put in the water and dip her hair in. Her hair turned red again.

She could once again sing with the golden bird and make the people have good dreams.

The princess and prince got married. The evil witch was so upset, she left the kingdom.

They lived happily ever after.

Name: ______________________ Date: ______________

1. **Write the sentences in the correct order to retell the story.**

Ⓐ The princess and prince got married and lived happily ever after.
Ⓑ The princess had long red hair and they called her the Rose Princess.
Ⓒ The bird told her how to get her red hair back again.
Ⓓ In the beginning, the princess and bird sang at night and the villagers had good dreams.

1	
2	
3	
4	

2. **What is the main meaning behind the folktale?**

Ⓐ There are all kinds of princesses.
Ⓑ Princesses always marry princes.
Ⓒ Birds are magical.
Ⓓ Good wins over evil.

3. **Mark the sentence that shows how the prince helped save the day for the princess and villagers.**

Ⓐ Just then a prince came with a lock of the princess' hair and dropped it on the ground.
Ⓑ Her hair turned red again.
Ⓒ They lived happily ever after.
Ⓓ The evil witch was upset.

4. **What sentences do not go with the story?Mark all that apply.**

Ⓐ The bird sang with the princess at night.
Ⓑ The bird flew away to find the prince.
Ⓒ The witch was a good witch and loved the princess.
Ⓓ The prince saved the day.

5. What was the good thing about the ending that helped everyone? Write in your own sentences.

How the Lion and Mouse Became Friends

Once upon a time, in a far away jungle, lived the king of lions. All the other animals were in fear of the lion. He was the fiercest creature. He would spend his time hunting, eating other animals and sleeping. No one dared to go into his den. They were all afraid. One day a tiny timid mouse thought he would look in the cave where the lion lived. He peeped in the hole. He did not see the lion. He was not there. He went in. He saw the lion's paws large prints in the dirt.

Just then, he heard a noise. The mouse said to himself, "I must hide, or he will eat me!" The mouse hid. The lion came in his cave. He did not see the little mouse. The lion fell asleep.

He was snoring loud. The mouse was behind him. He wanted to get out. He had to go over the lion. When he got on the lion, the lion woke up! He roared and roared. The mouse got scared and ran all over the lion. The lion tried to get the mouse.

Then the mouse got brave and asked the lion not to eat him. The mouse said that if he did not eat him, he would help the lion anytime.

The lion thought how funny it was that a tiny mouse would do that. He laughed and let the mouse go.

A few days later, the jungle heard the lion roaring louder than ever before. It was a roar that shook the jungle floor. The lion was in a hunter's trap. He could not get out.

The tiny mouse heard the roaring and went to see if he could help. When he found the lion, he told him to sit still. The mouse ate the ropes of the trap and the lion got out.

They were best friends forever after that.

If you are little, it does not mean you cannot help if you need to.

Name: ______________________ Date: ______________

6. What was the first thing that happened in the fable?

Ⓐ The lion came into his cave.
Ⓑ The mouse went to see where the lion lived.
Ⓒ The mouse and the lion became friends.
Ⓓ The lion needed the mouse's help.

7. What did the lion do to the mouse?Write a sentence in your own words.

8. What happened at the end of the story that showed the mouse kept his promise? Mark all that are right.

Ⓐ The mouse ran far, far away.
Ⓑ The mouse helped save the lion.
Ⓒ The mouse ate the ropes on the trap.
Ⓓ The mouse had a party for the lion.

9. Fables show a moral, a good reason a thing happens. What is the moral of this fable? Reread the fable if you need to.

Ⓐ The bigger you are, the better it is.
Ⓑ The big animals always win.
Ⓒ You can be little and help someone.
Ⓓ A little mouse is better than a big lion.

10. Write the story in the right order.

Ⓐ The lion and mouse became best friends.
Ⓑ The mouse went to see where the lion lived.
Ⓒ The lion was in a trap.
Ⓓ The lion let the mouse go.

1	
2	
3	
4	

Name: ______________________ Date: ______________

Chapter 1

Lesson 3: Describing Characters

Describe how characters in a story respond to major events and challenges.

You can scan the QR code given below or use the url to access additional EdSearch resources including videos and mobile apps related to Describing Characters.

Describing Characters	
URL	QR Code
http://www.lumoslearning.com/a/rl23	

Javier and His Friends Fly a Kite

Javier, Joseph, Wayne and Mike are good friends. They like playing baseball, fishing, hiking, and making model airplanes.

One day the boys wanted to try something new. They had seen the huge kites being flown over the lake. None of them had ever flown a kite.

Javier asked his dad what they needed to do to learn how to fly a kite. His dad told Javier they needed to start with learning how to fly small kites first.

They all got their money together and went to the hobby store. Javier and Wayne wanted kites that had dragons on them. Joseph and Mike liked the ones with long tails. The boys agreed on a dragon kite with a long tail.

Now to find the right spot to try it out. Another problem came up. Javier wanted to go to the lake and do it like they had seen the other kites being flown. Wayne said it was ok with him. It was ok with Joseph, too. Mike had a problem with the idea. He wanted to do it in a park. He said the kite might go into the lake and fall in the water.

The boys talked about it. They made a list of things that could happen at the lake and things that could happen at the park.

The list showed them that the park was the best place. They went to the park. Their dragon kite went up high with its tail flying. They were so happy.

1. What did the boys decide they wanted to learn how to do?

Ⓐ Go surfing
Ⓑ Build a teepee
Ⓒ Fly a kite
Ⓓ Take swimming lessons

2. The boys had 2 problems in the story. What were they?

Ⓐ Where to buy the kite
Ⓑ What kind of kite to buy
Ⓒ Where to fly the kite
Ⓓ How much money to spend

Name: ______________________ Date: ______________

3. How did the boys solve the first problem?

Ⓐ They decided to buy a cat kite.
Ⓑ They decided to buy a kite that had a dragon and had a long tail.
Ⓒ They decided they did not want to buy a kite.
Ⓓ They decided to buy a kite from a different store.

4. How did the boys solve the second problem? Mark the best answer from the story.

Ⓐ They made a list of things that could happen at the lake and things that could happen at the park. The list showed them that the park was the best place. They went to the park. Their dragon kite went up high with its tail flying.
Ⓑ Javier asked his dad what they needed to do to learn how to fly a kite. His dad told Javier they needed to start with learning how to fly small kites first.

5. Fill in the blanks in the chart. Look back at the story for help if you need to.

	In Story	**Not in Story**
Boys want to learn how to fly a kite		
Boys do not have money		
Boys pick a dragon kite with short tail		
Boys fly the kite at a park		

Name: ______________________ Date: ______________

Learning How to Work in a Group

It can be hard to work in a group. Some people like to do work by themselves.

Mrs. Taylor told her class they would make a project in groups. Each group would make a different kind of house. She picked which students would work with each other.

Marilyn, Alberto, D'Shawna and Sam were put in one group.

Sam and Alberto did not like each other. They lived on the same street and their brothers did not get along. When she called out their names, they both made ugly faces. Mrs. Taylor did not know about how they felt. She was trying to get kids to learn to get along better in class.

Marilyn and D'Shawna were fine with being in the group. Marilyn knew that D'Shawna was very smart and could help the group.

The teams had to pick who would do what part of the project. D'Shawna took over. She would do the writing. Marilyn would do the speaking. D'Shawna told Alberto and Sam they would make the log cabin together.

The boys grunted to show they did not like the idea. D'Shawna set up rules to go by. She said the boys did not have to talk but had to do their part. At first, they did not speak. They did start talking by the second week. D'Shawna had the team play little games to help them get along. They even started laughing with each other.

The project took 3 weeks in class to make. By the end of it, they boys were friends.

6. In this story, what was the problem?

Ⓐ The group did not know how to make a log cabin.
Ⓑ No one wanted to work together.
Ⓒ Alberto and Sam did not want to work together.
Ⓓ Mrs. Taylor was sick.

7. Who helped the group the most?

Ⓐ Mrs. Taylor
Ⓑ Marilyn
Ⓒ Sam
Ⓓ D'Shawna

7.1 What did D'Shawna do? Write your own paragraph.

8. Pick 4 things that helped the group do the project.

Ⓐ Mrs. Taylor let them work on their own.
Ⓑ D'Shawna made a good leader.
Ⓒ Setting rules was a good idea.
Ⓓ Not having to talk at first helped the boys do the work.
Ⓔ Marilyn was acting up.
Ⓕ Log cabins are easy to make.

9. Choose the correct word from the story. Look back at the story for help.

Mrs. Taylor did not know about how they ______________ . She was trying to get kids to learn to get along ______________ in class.

10. Did Mrs. Taylor's idea of group projects work with this team?

Ⓐ No
Ⓑ Yes
Ⓒ A Little Bit
Ⓓ Only for Marilyn and D'Shawna

Name: ______________________ Date: ______________

Chapter 1

Lesson 4: Figurative Language

Describe how words and phrases (e.g., regular beats, alliteration, rhymes, repeated lines) supply rhythm and meaning in a story, poem, or song.

You can scan the QR code given below or use the url to access additional EdSearch resources including videos and mobile apps related to Figurative Language.

edSearch

Figurative Language

URL	QR Code
http://www.lumoslearning.com/a/rl24	

Name: ____________________ Date: ____________

Going fishing

It's a great day to go fishing with Dad.
Get our poles and head to the lake.
Mom says -the bait -don't forget to take!
Spotty, the dog can't go-he's sad.

It's off to the lake, early in the day.
We stop near a shady, cool spot.
That way we won't get too hot.
Poles in the water to wait and hurray!

A bite first off, my pole dipping down.
Pulling and tucking, a keeper for sure!
Oh, no, don't take my lure!
What a big fish to take back to town!

A speckled fish, yellow and brown!

1. How do the rhymes help you better understand the poem? Choose the best answer.

Ⓐ The rhyming words help by giving meaning to the poem and drawing pictures in your mind to understand it.
Ⓑ The rhyming words are not helpful.
Ⓒ The rhyming words make you think of things other than fishing.
Ⓓ The poem does not have rhyming words in it.

2. What is the rhyming pattern for the first, second and third verses?

Ⓐ The first, third lines rhyme and the second, fourth lines rhyme
Ⓑ All lines rhyme in the poem.
Ⓒ None of the lines rhyme.
Ⓓ The first, fourth lines rhyme and the second,third lines rhyme.

3. Which words in the poem rhyme with clown? Write them.

Name: ______________________ Date: ______________

4. **How can you make the following sentence more vivid? (Alliteration) Choose the best answer.**

"A bite first off, my pole dipping down."

Ⓐ A bite, my pole went down.
Ⓑ A bite first off, my pole barely dipping down.
Ⓒ A bite first off, my pole dipping dark deep down.
Ⓓ None of the above.

5. **Use the following start and fill in the poem to make it rhyme. Make the first two lines rhyme and the last two. Use these words- dream, seem, frog, log**

I love my dog!

He sits on a ______________

By the stream

He likes to ______________

Socks - By Bonnie McRae

His name is Socks.
I think that rocks!
He loves to climb,
Or spin around on a dime!
That's my Socks!

Up the nearest tree,
Look- the bird he can see!
Then down to the ground,
After the mouse he found!
That's the way it's going to be!

He's a happy cat!
And you know very fat!
Socks eats really a lot
Of all the food I bought!
But sleeps on a hat!

Now how about all that?

6. What is the main rhyme pattern, not including the last line?

Ⓐ All the lines have the same rhyme at the end.
Ⓑ The first, second and fifth lines rhyme and the third and fourth lines rhyme.
Ⓒ The poem does not have any rhyming words.
Ⓓ The first, third lines rhyme and the fourth and fifth lines rhyme.

7. What is the meaning of the poem? Write your own sentence.

8. Find the rhyming words at the ends of the lines in the second verse and list them in two groups.

First set of rhyming words	
Second set of rhyming words	

9. Which verse does the last line in the poem have a rhyme with?

Ⓐ The first verse has a rhyme like the last line.
Ⓑ The second verse has a rhyme like the last line.
Ⓒ There is nothing that has a rhyme like the last line.
Ⓓ The third verse has a rhyme like the last line.

10. Mark the things that Socks likes to do.

Ⓐ Socks likes to sleep on a bed.
Ⓑ Socks likes to climb trees and watch birds.
Ⓒ Socks likes to eat.
Ⓓ Socks sleeps all day.

Chapter 1

Lesson 5: How is it Written?

Describe the overall structure of a story, including describing how the beginning introduces the story and the ending concludes the action.

You can scan the QR code given below or use the url to access additional EdSearch resources including videos and mobile apps related to How is it Written?

edSearch

How is it Written?

URL	QR Code
http://www.lumoslearning.com/a/rl25	

Chloe Finds A Baby Chick

Chloe was staying at her Nana and Grandpa's house. She loved to help feed the animals. Nana and Grandpa had horses, and chickens.

Every day, Grandpa would ask her to help him with the animals outside. He would feed the horses first. Then he would feed the chickens.

Grandpa was a tall cowboy. He would whistle for the horses to come. The horses would run fast to the fence. Chloe helped him put the horse feed in the buckets and get the hose to fill up the water troughs. She really liked doing that.

When it was time to feed the chickens, Grandpa first looked for eggs in the chicken coop. Then he would make a sound like chickens and put out their feed.

This time, Chloe got to put out the feed. As she was doing that, she heard a "peep, peep, peep" sound. She was very excited. Chloe told her Grandpa, "Grandpa, do you hear that sound? Is it a baby chick?"

Grandpa listened. He laughed and said, "Yes, Chloe. Now where is it ? Let's look."

They looked all around the pen.

Just then, Chloe saw the little yellow chick in a corner of the pen. "Here, Grandpa, here it is!", she shouted.

Grandpa came and slowly picked up the chick. Chloe thought it was so cute.

Grandpa put it in a coop by one of the hens. Soon the hen snuggled the baby chick.

Chloe was so happy! What fun it was to visit and be a help to her Grandpa.

1. How does the start of the story help you to understand the ending? Choose the best answer.

Ⓐ Chloe is at her Nana and Grandpa's house and helps feed the animals outside, where she finds a baby chick.
Ⓑ Chloe feeds the animals outside.
Ⓒ Chloe likes to help.
Ⓓ The start of the story does not help you understand the ending.

Name: ______________________ Date: ______________

2. Put the story sentences in the correct order.

Ⓐ She hears a baby chick when she is feeding the chickens.
Ⓑ Chloe helps Grandpa feed and water the horses.
Ⓒ Chloe is staying at her Nana and Grandpa's house.
Ⓓ Grandpa picks up the baby chick and puts it by a hen.

1	
2	
3	
4	

3. Why is it important that the story begins with where Chloe is? Write your own sentence to answer this question.

4. Which of the following does NOT happen in the story?

Ⓐ Chloe and Grandpa feed the horses and chickens.
Ⓑ Chloe hears a baby chick.
Ⓒ Grandpa will not let Chloe help feed the chicks.
Ⓓ Grandpa puts the baby chick in a coop by a hen.

5. What part of the ending shows you that Chloe had a good time feeding animals and help - ing Grandpa. Mark two sentences.

Ⓐ Chloe was so happy!
Ⓑ Soon the hen snuggled the baby chick.
Ⓒ Let's look
Ⓓ What fun it was to visit and be a help to her Grandpa.

Jason Rides a Train

Jason and his friend, Tom, wanted to ride a train. They lived outside of Boston. Jason had never ridden on a train. Tom had, but only with his family. The boys asked their parents if they could ride the train into Boston on their own.

Tom's mother was fine with that. Jason's mother was not sure. She knew he had never been on a train. His mother was worried that something might happen to him. Jason begged her to go. His mother finally said he could go. She made sure she got tickets and set a time for them to go and to come back. The mothers gave the boys instructions on how to be sure they got back on time. Tom took his watch to be sure they knew the right time to take the train back.

The boys were so happy. They packed a lunch to take with them. Both mothers took them to the station. Jason and Tom got on the train. Jason walked to the seats by the window. Tom and Jason sat down and looked out the window.

The train took off. It was going so fast. The boys laughed at the trees passing by outside the window. Jason told Tom it was making him dizzy to watch. Tom agreed. Then in about thirty minutes, they were in Boston.

After they got off the train, they went to a nearby park. They had their lunch and played on the slide and swings. Tom looked at his watch. It was time to go back to get on the train. They ran all the way back to the train station. Jason and Tom heard the whistle blowing, "TOOT, TOOT, TOOT!" They almost missed their train ride home.

This time, Tom picked the seats. Again, they laughed at how fast the train was going. They were back at their home town in such a quick time. Their mothers were there waiting. They told them how much fun they had. Both boys hugged their mothers and thanked them. They now want to go again. It was a special day for Jason.

Name: ______________________ Date: ______________

6. **In the beginning of the story, what did the boys want to do? Choose the sentence.**

Ⓐ They wanted to go to the zoo with their parents.
Ⓑ They wanted to go to a nearby park.
Ⓒ They wanted to ride a train to Boston by themselves.
Ⓓ They wanted to take a trip to a store to shop for toys.

7. **Do you think the boys' mothers will let them go again by themselves? Why? Put the story sentences in the correct order.**

Ⓐ They made the trip and did not have any trouble.
Ⓑ They got in trouble and cannot go alone again
Ⓒ They followed their mothers' instructions.
Ⓓ The boys wanted to go on a train trip by themselves.
Ⓔ The boys acted up and did not get back on time.

1	
2	
3	
4	

8. **What is the ending of the story? Write your own paragraph.**

9. What made the boys run back to the train? Follow the story order to help you. Fill in the blank.

The boys ran back to the train station because it was time for their ____________________

____

9.1 How did they know it was time to go back to the train?

Write your own sentence.

10. Which sentences explain how the beginning of the story introduces the story? Mark two that apply.

Ⓐ The beginning of the story tells that the boys want to go on a train trip with their parents.
Ⓑ The beginning of the story gives you the idea of the story to help you understand the train trip.
Ⓒ The boys' mothers helped them with a plan to make sure they were safe to go and come back on their trip.
Ⓓ The start of the story does not follow the end of the story.

Chapter 1

Lesson 6: Point of View

Acknowledge differences in the points of view of characters, including by speaking in a different voice for each character when reading dialogue aloud.

You can scan the QR code given below or use the url to access additional EdSearch resources including videos and mobile apps related to Point of View

Point of View

URL	QR Code
http://www.lumoslearning.com/a/rl26	

Being a Ballerina

Tabitha and Melony had just started ballet classes. The girls had their own ballet shoes and everything. Each Wednesday they went after school to **Sally's School of Stars** to practice.

"We love Ms. Sally!" Tabitha would say. "She's the best!"

"You got that right!" Melony would reply.

One day at practice, Tabitha took a fall.

"Yikes, my leg hurts!" She yelled.

"Oh, no!" replied Melony. "What happened?"

"Help me, please, get Ms. Sally, NOW!" cried Tabitha.

Melony ran to the front of the class and tugged at Ms Sally.

"Dear, what is wrong?" asked Ms. Sally.

"HURRY! HURRY! HURRY! Tabitha is hurt BAD!" screamed Melony.

"OH, MY!"

Ms. Sally ran to find Tabitha.

Tabitha sat crying on the floor. "I don't know what happened." She whimpered. "It hurts really awful."

"Go get an ice pack for me, please, Melony. You know where they are, dear. Now, don't worry. I'm calling your mom on my cell, Tabitha." Ms. Sally said this in such a sweet calming voice. Tabitha quit crying when Melony put the ice pack where Ms. Sally said to put it. "Thanks," she said.

In a few minutes, Tabitha's mom came. She carried her to the car.

"Will you call us as soon as you know something, please?" asked Ms. Sally.

"Yes, of course." said Tabitha's mom.

Soon they got the call. It was just a sprained ankle. She would be fine in a few days.

"What a good thing to hear." sighed Ms. Sally.

1. How did Melony know that Tabitha was hurt? Which sentence helps you to know?

Ⓐ "We love Ms. Sally!"
Ⓑ "Thanks," she said.
Ⓒ "I don't know what happened."
Ⓓ "Help me, please, get Ms. Sally, NOW!" cried Tabitha.

2. What point of view (how the girls feel) is shown for Ms. Sally? Write your own sentence. Read the story again to help you frame your answer.

3. What can you tell by the things that Ms. Sally had to say? Choose 2 characteristics.

Ⓐ Ms. Sally was a kind and caring person.
Ⓑ Ms. Sally was not happy with the class.
Ⓒ Ms. Sally was worried about Tabitha getting hurt.
Ⓓ Ms. Sally did not listen to Melony.

4. Pretend that you are Melony. How would you say the following sentence?

"HURRY! HURRY! HURRY! Tabitha is hurt BAD!"

Ⓐ Very loud and with excitement
Ⓑ Very soft and calm
Ⓒ A little loud but not too much
Ⓓ Just read it, not loud or soft

5. Mark an x in the chart that shows which people said the statements.

	Ms. Sally	Melony	Tabitha
"Now, don't worry."	☐	☐	☐
"You got that right!"	☐	☐	☐
"It hurts really awful."	☐	☐	☐

Playing on a Team

Mike and Tim wanted to play on a soccer team. They had not played on a team before. The boys had played soccer together. They joined a team.

"Wow, this is going to be fun for us!" exclaimed Tim.

"I am a bit scared." replied Mike.

"Hey, you play well." Tim said.

"Yeah, but the other guys might be better than me." Mike was worried.

He wanted to be on a team, but he didn't want to make mistakes. He was afraid the other team members would make fun of him.

Tim told him, "Don't worry, just make it like they are all me. It'll be fine. You wait and see. Let's go to practice!"

The boys got to the field. They met the other players. The boys were all nice to them. No one was any better than Mike and Tim. Practice was fun.

"Told ya' so!" Tim yelled as they ran home.

"You were right! I'm not scared anymore!" Mike replied.

6. Which sentence shows that Mike was afraid?

Ⓐ Mike said, "Ok, let's go!"
Ⓑ They met the other players
Ⓒ "I am a bit scared." replied Mike.
Ⓓ They joined a team.

7. How can you tell that Tim is happy and looking forward to being on the soccer team? Pick 2 sentences.

Ⓐ "Wow, this is going to be fun for us!" exclaimed Tim.
Ⓑ Let's go to practice!
Ⓒ "Hey, you play well." Tim said.
Ⓓ Don't worry, just make like they are all me.

8. How did Mike feel after practice? Write your own sentence to explain.

9. What made Mike change his mind (point of view) about being scared?

Ⓐ The team gave him hugs.
Ⓑ The coach said he was great.
Ⓒ The other team players were nice to him.
Ⓓ He got an ice cream after practice.

10. Have your teacher come to you and read something out loud from the story that either Tim or Mike said. Pretend to be that person and read it like they would say it.

Name: ______________________ Date: ______________

Chapter 1

Lesson 7: I Can See It!

You can scan the QR code given below or use the url to access additional EdSearch resources including videos and mobile apps related to I Can See It!

I Can See It!

URL	QR Code
http://www.lumoslearning.com/a/rl27	

Name: ______________________ Date: ______________

Mimi and Her Spoons

Mimi was Adelle's grandmother. Adelle liked going to her house in Georgia. Mimi had many things in her huge house. She had teapots, quilts, plates, and spoons.

Spoons were Adelle's favorite. Mimi had them in boxes and special ones hanging on the wall on a rack.

Mimi told stories of her spoons to Adelle.

This was so much fun. Mimi loved spending time with her.

Mimi said, "Adelle, now look at these on the wall. They came from many places. Some are from states here in the U.S. Others are from far away countries I have visited."

Adelle replied, "Tell me, Mimi, tell me all about them."

She began, "Ok, let's see. There are ten spoons on this rack.

The first and last ones are from Finland. They were brought here by my grandmother. The second and sixth ones are from Denmark. We have family there, too. The third one is from Mississippi where I was born. The fourth one is from Texas where you live. The fifth one is just a fun one of Elvis. I loved his songs. The seventh one is from Arkansas, a very pretty place. The eighth one is from Pennsylvania. I went there with your mother once. The ninth one is from an Indian reservation in Oklahoma.

Mimi told me the stories of each of them. She had so many good stories to tell of the places she had been and family members.

Name: ______________________ Date: ______________

1. Who are the characters in this story? List them.

2. Put the spoons in the right order as they appear in the picture (wall rack) and story.

1. Elvis
2. Denmark
3. Oklahoma
4. Arkansas
5. Mississippi
6. Finland
7. Texas
8. Pennsylvania
9. Finland
10. Denmark

1	
2	
3	
4	
5	
6	
7	
8	
9	
10	

Name: ______________________ Date: ____________

3. What kind of relationship do Mimi and Adelle have? Write a sentence.

4. Which answer tells the setting of the story?

Ⓐ Mimi had them in boxes and special ones hanging on the wall on a rack.
Ⓑ Mimi told stories of her spoons to Adelle.
Ⓒ Adelle liked going to her house in Georgia. Mimi had many things in her huge house.
Ⓓ The first and last ones are from Finland.

5. Which are important parts to the story and picture?

Ⓐ The stories behind the spoons.
Ⓑ The fact that Mimi had been many places.
Ⓒ Adelle had fun listening to Mimi talk about the spoons.
Ⓓ The Elvis spoon is just for fun.

Papa, Taylor, and Marie

Every year Papa was happy when his granddaughters would come to visit him on the farm.

The best time was when Papa took both Taylor and Marie to ride the horse, Pepper.

Taylor was about 4 years old. Marie was 12.

"Oh boy, Papa! I am wearing a cowboy hat!" She said.

Papa said, "You look good in it."

Marie chimed in, "Yep, you do!"

Papa put the girls on the horse.

Taylor turned to Marie.

"Yippee!"

Marie replied, "Don't wiggle or we will fall off!"

Taylor just smiled.

Papa first walked the girls around leading Pepper.

He wanted to be sure they were ok with riding by themselves.
Marie told him to give her the reins and let go.

He let go and the girls had a great ride!

6. What can you tell by the picture and the story? Mark 2 sentences.

Ⓐ Papa loved when his granddaughters came to visit.
Ⓑ Taylor did not want to ride the horse.
Ⓒ Marie was wearing a cowboy hat.
Ⓓ The girls had a good time on the horse.

7. What is the setting of the story?

Ⓐ At Taylor's house
Ⓑ Somewhere in a city
Ⓒ On Papa's farm
Ⓓ The story does not say.

8. How do the picture and story help you know what happens in the story (plot)? Write your answer in a sentence.

9. Which sentence shows that Marie wants to be sure they do not fall off?

Ⓐ Marie replied, "Don't wiggle or we will fall off!"
Ⓑ Marie told him to give her the reins and let go.
Ⓒ Marie chimed in, "Yep, you do!"
Ⓓ Marie was 12.

10 .What is the order of the story?

Ⓐ Papa let the reins go and they girls rode by themselves.
Ⓑ Marie told Taylor not to wiggle.
Ⓒ Papa put the girls on Pepper.
Ⓓ Papa walked the girls around while they were on the horse.

Chapter 1

Lesson 8: Alike and Different

Theme: the main idea of a story.
Setting: the time and place in which the story takes place.
Plot: the most important actions, plans or events taking place in a story that support the main idea or theme of the story.
Supporting statements: text that explains or adds more detail to the theme (main idea). For instance, giving examples.

Cheater Pants and Junie B. Jones and the Mushy, Gushy Valentine by Barbara Park, both starring Junie B. Jones in the Junie B. Jones series, will be used as examples for how you might meet the requirements of this standard.

Publisher's Note: Here are some suggestions for how you might write text that does what the standard asks for.
1. Before you can compare and contrast anything, you must first identify the themes (main ideas), settings (times and places) plots and supporting statements.
2. After doing step 1, you need to figure out what is the same or similar about the themes, settings and plots, in both stories, and what is different about them.

Compare and contrast.

Compare: describe similarities between the two texts in important points and key details.
Contrast: describe the differences between the two texts in important points and key details.

You can scan the QR code given below or use the url to access additional EdSearch resources including videos and mobile apps related to *Alike and Different*.

Alike and Different

URL	QR Code
http://www.lumoslearning.com/a/rl29	

Name: ______________________ Date: ______________

Story #1-Goldilocks and the Three Bears, adaptation version 1

Read the two stories and answer the questions.Reread as many times as you need to.

Once upon a time there were three bears, a papa, a mama and a baby. They were going to eat. Their porridge was too hot to eat, so they went for a walk.

Goldilocks came along and went into their house.

She was hungry and saw the food. Papa Bear's porridge was too hot. Mama Bear's porridge was too cold. Baby Bear's porridge was just right. She ate all of it!

Goldilocks wanted to rest. She saw 3 chairs. Papa Bear's chair was too hard. Mama Bear's chair was too soft. Baby Bear's chair was just right. But, Goldilocks broke it!

She was tired. Goldilocks saw 3 beds. Papa Bear's bed was too hard. Mama Bear's bed was too soft. Baby Bear's bed was just right. She went fast sleep.

Then, the 3 bears came home. They saw what happened to the porridge, the chair, and Goldilocks in the bed.

The bears roared.

Goldilocks woke up and jumped out a window, running all the way home.

Story #2-Goldilocks, rewritten from memory

Once upon a time there were three bears who lived in a cottage in the woods. Papa Bear, Mama Bear and Baby Bear. The bears loved a good healthy breakfast. One morning, Mama Bear cooked porridge.

It was too hot to eat, so they went for a walk while it cooled off.

A pretty girl, Goldilocks, had gone into the woods alone. She smelled the food.

She went up to the cottage. No one answered her knock on the door. She went inside.

Here Goldilocks saw three bowls of porridge. She was hungry. She tried the first bowl. It was too hot. She tried the second bowl. It was too cold. She tried the third bowl. It was just right. She ate it all!

Then she saw three chairs. She sat in the first chair. It was too hard. She tried the second chair. It was too soft. She sat in the third chair. It was just right, but it broke!

Goldilocks was getting very sleepy after eating all the porridge. She looked for a bed. She found three beds. The first bed was too high and the second was too low. The third bed was just right. She laid down and went to sleep.

The bears got home and saw their porridge. Papa Bear and Mama Bear said, "Someone's been eating my porridge". Baby Bear said, "Someone's been eating my porridge and it's all gone!"

Then they saw their chairs. Papa and Mama Bear said, "Someone's been sitting in my chair." Baby Bear said, "Someone's been sitting in my chair and it's broken!"

Now they decided to take naps. When they saw their beds, Papa Bear and Mama Bear said, "Someone's been sleeping in my bed". Baby Bear said, "Someone's been sleeping in my bed and she's still there!"

This woke Goldilocks! She was so scared. She ran out of the cottage and all the way home. She said she would never go far away alone again!

1. Why did the bears go for a walk?

Ⓐ They needed to check the forest.
Ⓑ They were doing their exercises.
Ⓒ Their porridge was too hot to eat.
Ⓓ They liked to go for walks.

2. Why did Goldilocks eat the porridge? Write your own sentence.

3. Where did the bears find Goldilocks?

Ⓐ Eating porridge
Ⓑ Walking around the cottage
Ⓒ Asleep in a bed
Ⓓ Sitting in a chair

Name: ______________________ Date: ______________

4. Which sentence best tells about Goldilocks?

Ⓐ A pretty girl, Goldilocks, had gone into the woods alone.
Ⓑ She found three beds.
Ⓒ She sat in the first chair.
Ⓓ The third bed was just right.

5. What did the bears say? Pick 3.

Ⓐ "Someone's here."
Ⓑ "Someone's been eating my porridge."
Ⓒ "Someone's been sitting in my chair."
Ⓓ "Someone's been sleeping in my bed."

6. What did Goldilocks decide to do at the end of the story?Mark your answer.

Ⓐ She decided to play with her dolls.
Ⓑ She decided to go back to the bear's cottage.
Ⓒ She decided to take another nap.
Ⓓ She decided never to go in the woods alone again.

7. What is the biggest difference in the two stories?

Ⓐ The second story has the bears talking.
Ⓑ The first story is harder to read.
Ⓒ The first story is more exciting to read.
Ⓓ There is no difference.

8. Fill in the chart with correct answers. Some things may be in both stories.

	Story #1	**Story #2**
Bears went for a walk.	☐	☐
Goldilocks broke the little bear's chair.	☐	☐
Goldilocks jumped out the window.	☐	☐
Goldilocks will never go into the woods by herself again.	☐	☐

9. Write the correct answers that are found in both Story 1 and Story 2. Read the stories again if you need to.
There were 3 of each of these.

10. What is the difference between the ending in Story 1 and the ending in Story 2? Write your answer.

End of Reading: Literature

Answer Key and Detailed Explanations

Chapter 1: Reading: Literature

Lesson 1: The Question Session

Question No.	Answer	Detailed Explanations
1	D	The best answer is D. It includes all of those that went to the beach. Answer A and B only include some of those and is not correct. Answer C cannot be found in the story and is incorrect.
2	B, C, D, G	Dog leash, shells, and purse were not listed as things that Sara took to the beach. They are not correct. Sunscreen, sand shovel and tools and bathing suit are listed and are correct.
3	C	They had been in the water before and Dad said they could go back in. The water is correct. The table, the van and none of the above are not correct, as they are not in the story details.
4	-	Sample Answer: They went home because it was getting dark. At the end of the story it is noted that it was getting dark. That would be the reason they went home. The student must say that in his/her sentence, but word choice can vary.
5	-	1. happy 2. smiling 3. nice 4. having fun 5. laughed Other correct words: fun, funny, smiled, wonderful time. Students choose words from the story to show that it was a good time. Those listed are found in the story. Students' need to use 5 of those listed.
6	B	Answer B is found in the story and tells what they wanted to do and liked to do. Answer A,C and D are not found in the story and are not correct.
7.	-	Sample Answer: Today, the girls could not go outside because the wind was blowing, and it looked like rain. (example can be slightly different in wording) In the second sentence it explains that the girls were worried because the wind was blowing, and it looked like it might rain. The student's sentence needs to have these words or similar words in them.
8	B, C, D, E	Sentences 2,3,4,5 are all details found in the story. They are all correct. Sentence 1 is not in the story and did not happen. It is not correct.

Question No.	Answer	Detailed Explanations
9	B	The second sentence, "The girls were not happy", tells how they felt when they could not go outside. The other sentences are in the story, but do not answer the question asked.
10	-	Sentence A and D tell details about the story and should be marked "Yes". Sentences B and C are not correct details from the story and are wrong answers.

Lesson 2: Recount stories

Question No.	Answer	Detailed Explanations
1	-	The story begins with the princess and her name, so sentence #2 should be first. Then the story states how the princess and bird sang at night. The clue for the sentence to be second is "in the beginning". The bird then told her how to get her hair back to red when the witch cast the spell. It should go third. The last sentence should be they got married and lived happily ever after, as that is the ending of the story.
2	D	The main idea is that good wins over evil. The fourth answer is the only correct one that is the main idea of the folktale. The first answer is not given. The second answer is not supported, and neither is the third.
3	A	All of the sentences are details in the story, but sentence A is the correct one. It tells exactly what the prince did. The story goes on to say that because of that a rose bush grew.
4	B,C	The first and fourth sentences are details from the story. They are correct. The second and third sentences are not in the story.
5	-	Answers will vary. Some may include that the prince saved the day, the princess got her red hair back, the witch was upset, they got married.
6	B	The first thing that happened in the story was that the mouse went to see where the lion lived. It is in the second paragraph. The other details happened later. The second sentence is correct.
7	-	Answers will vary. An example of a correct answer should include that the lion tried to get the mouse, the lion let the mouse go, or that the lion did not eat the mouse.
8	B,C	The lion got in a trap and the mouse saved him by eating through the trap ropes. The second and third sentences are the only correct ones. The first, and fourth sentences are not listed in the story and are not a part of it.
9	C	The story states, "If you are little, it does not mean you cannot help if you need to." The third sentence is correct. It is the moral of the story in different words.
10	-	The sequence of the story is that the mouse went to see where the lion lived, the lion let the mouse go, the lion got in a trap, and the lion and mouse became best friends. The correct order is sentence 2,4,3,1.

Name: ______________________ Date: ______________

Lesson 3: Describing Characters

Question No.	Answer	Detailed Explanations
1	C	The story states that the boys wanted to learn how to fly a kite. The third answer is correct. The other answers are not found in the story.
2	B, C	The story states that the boys first did not know what kind of kite to get and then did not know where to fly their kite. The second and third answers are correct. The first and fourth answers are not found in the story and are not correct.
3	B	Some of the boys wanted a dragon kite. Others wanted one with a long tail. They decided to buy one that had a long tail and was a dragon. The second sentence is correct and found in the story. The other sentences are not found in the story and are not correct.
4	A	The first paragraph is the best answer as it is the solution found in the story. The second choice has nothing to do with the second problem.
5	-	The first and fourth phrases are details in the story and should be marked, "in story". The second and third phrases are not in the story and should be marked, "not in story".
6	C	The major event in the story was that the group had to work together to make a project. Alberto and Sam did not like each other. Mrs. Taylor put them in the same group. The third sentence is the best answer. The first, second and fourth sentences are not found in the story. They are not correct.
7	D	D'Shawna led the group. She helped the boys work together. Mrs. Taylor gave the assignment. Marilyn worked well but did not help the boys. Sam did not want to be with Alberto. The correct answer is D'Shawna.
7.1	-	Answers will vary. They should include that she told the boys they would make the log cabin. She set rules. She said they did not have to talk to each other. She had them work together even if they did not want to. She had the team play games every day to get them to get along better.
8	A,B,C,D	The first 4 sentences give details from the story and are correct. The last 2 sentences are not found and are not correct.
9	felt,better	These are the vocabulary words found in the story and must be exact to be correct.
10	B	Yes, the idea worked as can be seen in the conclusion of the story. The second answer is correct. The others do not apply.

Lesson 4: Figurative Language

Question No.	Answer	Detailed Explanations
1	A	The first sentence is the best answer, as the rhyming words help the story to flow and give details to help the reader picture the event happening. The second, third and fourth answers are incorrect as they do not back up the poem or its meaning.
2	D	In each verse (except the last line), the first and fourth lines rhyme and the second and third lines rhyme. The last answer is correct.
3	-	The words that rhyme with clown in the poem are down, town, brown and are the only correct answers.
4	C	Alliteration means a way of adding more interest by using words with the same consonant sound at the beginning of them. The third sentence does this with dipping dark deep down. It is the correct answer.
5	log,dream	The rhymes must be dog, log and then stream, dream, to make sense and rhyme.
6	B	In all the verses, except the last line, the rhyme pattern is first, second, fifth and third, fourth. The second answer is the only correct one.
7	-	Answers will vary. The student may say that the poem is about a person's cat and how it acts. The answer should refer to the cat and may give details about him.
8	-	In the second verse there are two sets of rhyming words, the words tree, see, be are at the end of lines 1,2,5. The second set of words ground, found are at the ends of line 3,4.
9	D	The third verse has the rhyming words of fat, hat, so that rhymes with it. The other verses do not have "at" rhymes in them and are not correct.
10	B, C	These two answers list the things socks likes to do. The other answers mention things not in the poem.

Name: ______________________ Date: ______________

Lesson 5: How is it Written?

Question No.	Answer	Detailed Explanations
1	A	The first answer is the best answer because it states the setting and tells you what Chloe does to help out and what she finds. The second and third animals are details but do not explain. The fourth answer does not follow the story line.
2	C, B, A, D	First stated in the story is that Chloe is at her Nana and Grandpa's house. Then the story goes on to say she helps feed and water the horses. Next, she hears a baby chick and last Grandpa picks up the chick. This is the correct story sequence.
3	-	Answers will vary but should include that the story setting shows where Chloe is when the story happens and helps you to understand what happens all the way to the end.
4	C	The third sentence is the only one that is NOT found in the story and is the correct answer.
5	A, D	The last two sentences in the story show that she had a good time. The first and fourth sentences should be marked. The second and third sentences do not show that she had a good time and are only details in the story.
6	C	The beginning of the story tells that the boys wanted to take a train ride to Boston by themselves.
7	D, C, A	-
8	-	Answers will vary but should include the following. The boys wanted to go to on a train ride by themselves. Their parents made a plan for them. The boys took the train, went to the park and got back on the train.
9	-	The boys ran back to the train because it was time for their train to go back home. The story states, "It was time to go back to get on the train".
9.1	-	The story states that they knew it was time because Tom looked at his watch. Answers will vary but should include that he looked at his watch.
10	B, C	The second and third sentences give information that shows how the beginning of the story helps the story to be introduced and are correct. The first and fourth sentences do not follow the story and are not correct.

Name: ______________________ Date: ______________

Lesson 6: Point of View

Question No.	Answer	Detailed Explanations
1	D	The fourth sentence is a detail that was used to show Melony that Tabitha was hurt. It is the correct answer. The other quotes do not show that and are not correct.
2	-	Answer will vary but should include that the girls say that they love her, she is the best or similar answers to that.
3	A, C	The story narrative shows that Ms. Sally was kind and caring. It also shows that she was worried. The first and third sentences are correct. The second and fourth sentences are not shown in the narrative of the story and are not correct.
4	A	The sentence is written in capital letters and with explanation marks. This shows that it should be read very loud and with excitement. The first sentence is the only correct one.
5	-	Ms. Sally said the first quote, Melony said the second one and Tabitha said the third one. They should be marked accordingly.
6	C	In the third sentence Mike says that he is scared. That is the correct answer. The first, second and fourth sentences do not use vocabulary that shows he is afraid.
7	A, B	In the first and second sentences, exclamation marks are used to show excitement. The tone of voice can be read in the sentences. They are the correct answers. The third and fourth sentences do not show excitement and are not correct.
8	-	Answers will vary but should say that Mike was not scared anymore or that he was happy he went to practice.
9	C	The third sentence is stated in the story and is correct. None of the other sentences are found in the story and they are not correct.
10	-	This question involves teacher participation and must be oral for credit to be given. The standard states that the student must read orally to show speaking in a different voice.

Lesson 7: I Can See It!

Question No.	Answer	Detailed Explanations
1	-	1. Mimi 2. Adelle Characters are the people in the story. Mimi and Adelle are the only characters in this story.
2	-	1. Finland 2. Denmark 3. Mississippi 4. Texas 5. Elvis 6. Denmark 7. Arkansas 8. Pennsylvania 9. Oklahoma 10.Finland Using the story and picture, you can put the spoons in the order they appear.
3	-	Answer will vary but should state something to the effect that they love each other and have a good relationship.
4	C	The third answer is correct. It states that the setting is at Mimi's house in Georgia.
5	A, B, C	The 1,2,3 sentences are important to the story and picture. They are the correct answers, and should all be marked. The fourth sentence is not important and is incorrect.
6	A, D	The picture and story show that Papa loved his granddaughters to come visit and the girls had a good time on the horse. The first and fourth sentences are correct. The second and third sentences are not in the story and are not correct.
7	C	The first paragraph shows the setting as being on a farm. The picture is also of a farm. The third answer is correct. The others are not correct.
8	-	Answers will vary but should include the picture shows the girls on a horse and the story tells about them riding the horse at their Papa's farm. In that way the picture helps you to understand the story.

Question No.	Answer	Detailed Explanations
9	A	The first sentence is correct as it states that Marie tells Taylor not to wiggle or they will fall off. The other sentences do not say anything about making sure they do not fall off. They are not correct.
10	C, B, D, A	The order of the story is that Papa put the girls on the horse, Marie told Taylor not to wiggle, he walked them around while they were on the horse and then he let the reins go.

Lesson 8: Alike and Different

Question No.	Answer	Detailed Explanations
1	C	The fairy tale states that the porridge was hot. It is stated that is why they went for a walk. The third sentence is correct. The other answers are not found and are not correct.
2	-	Answers will vary. The correct answer should say the she was hungry, as that is a detail in the story.
3	C	The story states that she was found asleep in a bed. The third answer is correct. The other answers are not found and are not correct.
4	A	The first sentence describes Goldilocks and is correct. The other sentences give details, but do not tell about her and are not correct.
5	B, C, D	The first sentence is not in the story. The second, third and fourth ones are in the story and are the correct answers.
6	D	The fourth answer is found in the story and is correct. The other answers are not found and are not correct.
7	A	The first sentence is correct. The first story does not have any narrative. The second sentence is not correct because the first story has lower vocabulary and is easier to read. The third sentence is not correct because the second story has more elaboration and is more exciting. The fourth sentence is not correct because although the main plot is the same, there are many differences in the 2 stories.
8	-	Sentence 1 and 2 are details found in both stories and should be marked in both columns. Sentence 3 is only in the first story and only that column should be marked. Sentence 4 is only in the second story and only that column should be marked.
9	-	Both stories have 3 bears, bowls of porridge, chairs and beds. Those are the only correct answers.
10	-	Answers will vary but must include that in Story 1 Goldilocks jumped out of the window and in Story 2, she ran out of the cottage.

Chapter 2 - Reading Informational Text

The objective of the Reading Informational Text standards is to ensure that the student is able to read and comprehend informational texts (history/social studies, science, and technical texts) related to Grade 2.

To help students master the necessary skills, information to help the student understand the concepts related to the standard is given. Along with this, we encourage the student to go through the resources available online on EdSearch to gain an in depth understanding of these concepts. The EdSearch page for each lesson can be accessed with the help of the url or the QR code provided.

A small map is provided after each passage or text in which the student can enter the details as understood from the literary text. Doing this will help the student to refer to key points that help in answering the questions with ease.

Chapter 2

Lesson 1: Ask and answer questions

You can scan the QR code given below or use the url to access additional EdSearch resources including videos and mobile apps related to *Ask and answer questions*

Ask and answer questions

URL	QR Code
http://www.lumoslearning.com/a/ri21	

BBQ Pit

This is a picture of a BBQ pit. It is used for cooking many kinds of meat. Some kinds are beef, chicken, turkey, and pork.

They come in different sizes. This one is a large one. Some people use them for cooking during holidays, cook-off contests, big parties, and at restaurants. It can hold a huge amount of meat.

The pit is made of metal. It is a homemade pit. Homemade pits are made by people at their houses. They do not come from a store and are not made in a factory.

It is placed on a trailer, so it can be moved around on wheels. This BBQ pit is too heavy to try to move without it being on a trailer.

It has an oven, a temperature gauge, a fire box and a smokestack. It also has a wood rack outside of the pit to place things on such as pans, and cooking utensils. The oven holds the meat on a rack. The temperature gauge shows how hot the oven is cooking. The fire box is where the wood is put and lit to make the heat in the oven. The smokestack is for the smoke to go out while it is cooking.

BBQ pits are very useful to many people.

1. What are some kinds of meat cooked on BBQ pits? Pick the best answer.

Ⓐ Chicken, turkey, and beef
Ⓑ Turkey and chicken
Ⓒ Beef, chicken, turkey and pork
Ⓓ Pork, and beef

Name: ______________________ Date: ______________

2. How is a homemade BBQ pit different from one from a store?

Homemade pits are made by people at their ....They do not come from

a...and are not made in a ....

3. Why is a big BBQ pit placed on a trailer? Write your own sentence.

4. What is this passage about? Pick the best answer.

Ⓐ It tells about how to make a BBQ pit.
Ⓑ It tells the main information about a large BBQ pit.
Ⓒ It tells about how to cook on a BBQ pit.
Ⓓ It tells how to heat up a BBQ pit.

5. Mark some of the uses of a large BBQ in the box given below.

	Yes	**No**
Cooking for the holidays	□	□
Making frozen desserts	□	□
Restaurants	□	□
BBQ contests	□	□
Big parties	□	□

Farmall Tractor

Here is a picture of a tractor. Tractors are used by many people. Some tractors are used by farmers, or those who mow large areas for a living. This tractor has a blade on the back for mowing.

Mr. McRae bought this tractor to mow his fields. He has horses in the field. Sometimes weeds grow up in the field. The horses cannot eat the weeds. The weeds would make them sick. So, he mows them down. He does this about 2 times a month.

He also uses his tractor to plow his garden for planting. Mr. McRae makes 4 rows for planting. He plants corn, tomatoes, potatoes, and peppers. Plowing the garden is only done 2 times a year for each time he has a garden.

Look carefully at the picture and answer the questions.

6. What is this tractor used for?

Fill in the blanks with words that come from the story.

This tractor is used to ______________ and ______________

7. Identify the different users of tractors? Use the story to find the best answer.

Ⓐ Some tractors are used by farmers, or those who mow large areas for a living.
Ⓑ Some tractors are used by teenagers.
Ⓒ Some tractors are used by sailors.
Ⓓ Some tractors are used by children.

8. Fill in the chart to show where you would find tractors.

	Yes	No
Out in the country		
On a farm		
In a mall		
On a ranch		

9. What did Mr. McRae plant in his garden?

10. Why does Mr. McRae mow his fields where the horses stay? Write a sentence.

Chapter 2

Lesson 2: The Main idea

Main idea: the most important idea (or ideas) in a text. Sometimes called the theme of the text. The main idea can be the purpose of the author in writing the text (for example, an attempt to persuade you to agree with the author's opinion), or just to entertain you (for example, telling a funny story). Supporting statements: text that explains or adds more detail to the main idea (for instance, giving examples).

Let us understand the concept with an example.

School Uniforms: A Good Idea
By Emily Adams

I think school uniforms would be good for all schools, because they can cause changes that make a school better. How? By stopping kids from judging other kids by the clothes they wore. Also, by making a good impression about the school because all students would be wearing nice looking uniforms.
Judging people by the clothes they wear would stop for sure if uniforms were required in the school. Let's say someone wore an outfit that was different from the clothes most kids wore. If the clothes were very fashionable and expensive, some kids would be jealous, or if the clothes were "not cool," some kids would think they were inferior. Some kids are criticized for being sloppy in the way they wear their clothes – shirts not tucked in, pants that sag below the waist or prewashed jeans with rips in them. Uniforms would prevent this appearance.

It would be better if kids judged each other by who they were, not by what they wore. If kids were all wearing the same uniform, there would not be a reason to judge anyone based on their clothing. But what if kids wanted to personalize their uniforms so they could look a little different? The school's dress code could allow different accessories. For example, if a student liked glitter, she could add a glittery bow or a cute belt. Or an athlete could wear a button or belt with a team logo.

To sum it all up, uniforms are the best choice for the school because they eliminate kids judging each other by what they wear, and they create a nice, similar look for all kids attending that school.

Determine the main idea of a text.
The main idea of this text is to give a positive opinion about school uniforms.

Recount the key details and explain how they support the main idea.
By stopping kids from judging other kids by the clothes they wore. Also, by making a good impression about the school because all students would be wearing nice looking uniforms. It would encourage kids to judge each other by who they were, not by what they wore.

You can scan the QR code given below or use the url to access additional EdSearch resources including videos and mobile apps related to *The Main Idea*.

The Main Idea

URL	QR Code
http://www.lumoslearning.com/a/ri22	

Facts About Tropical Rainforests

Read the passage. Answer the questions. The paragraphs are numbered to help you with the questions.

1. Tropical rainforests are homes to many animals and people, and help support our lives. Rainforests are hot, rainy places with lots of huge trees. The plants have many leaves. They are found in places like Central and South America, Africa, Asia and Australia.

2. When scientists talk about rainforests, they talk about the three sections or layers of them. The bottom layer is called the "ground layer". Here people, animals, and plants live. The ground is lush and damp. The next layer is the "understory" which is bushy. You can find trees and animals in this layer, too. The top is called the "canopy". It is very thick. Very little light gets in, so the rainforest is dark. The canopy is the protection for the rainforest.

3. If you look down from an airplane on a rainforest it looks like a big green carpet or green grass everywhere. The plants from the rainforests help the world to breathe. They make oxygen for us. We need this to breathe.

4. Many animals and insects live in rainforests on the bottom, understory or canopy levels. There are monkeys, parrots, toucans, birds, jaguars, snakes, butterflies, frogs, anteaters, and ants.

5. Beautiful plants live there, too. Flowers like the hibiscus, orchid, and passion flower thrive in rainforests.

6. The rainforests are home to lakes, streams, and rivers. Here live other creatures like crocodiles, water lizards, turtles, snakes, and fish.

7. People in tribes have called the rainforests their home for centuries. They can find most everything they need to live on right in the rainforests.

8. Groups are helping to keep the rainforests alive for the people and animals there and for us to keep fresh air on earth.

1. What is the main topic of this article?

Ⓐ The article is about crocodiles.
Ⓑ The article is about tribes in rainforests.
Ⓒ The article is about how people are helping the rainforests.
Ⓓ The article gives facts about rainforests.

Name: ______________________ Date: ______________

2. Fill in the blank to show the main topic.

______________________ are homes to many animals, people, and help support our lives.

3. List the types of flowers in paragraph 5.

4. Fill in the chart with details from paragraph 4 and 6.

	Lives in water or on land	Land
snakes	☐	☐
monkeys	☐	☐
jaguars	☐	☐
parrots	☐	☐

5. Underline the topic sentence from paragraph 2.

2. When scientists talk about rainforests, they talk about the three sections or layers of them. The bottom layer is called the "ground layer." Here live people, animals, and plants. The ground is lush and damp. The next layer is the "understory," which is bushy. You can find trees and animals in this layer, too. The top is called the "canopy." It is very thick. Very little light gets in, so the rainforest is dark. The canopy is the protection for the rainforest.

Name: ______________________________ Date: ________________

Planting Flowers

Read the information and answer the questions. The paragraphs are numbered to help with questions and answers.

1. Flowers are pretty to look at and can be easily planted.
2. In this article, you will learn about planting flowers that are ready to bloom.
3. The best kind of flowers to grow will depend on where you live, and the kind of light the flower needs. It is important to plant the flower in the right light or it may not grow at all. Flowers need different kind of light to grow. These are full sunlight, partial sunlight, partial shade or full shade. Plants come with a tag to help you.
4. Some favorite flowers are zinnias, petunias, lilies, marigolds and begonias, daisies and sunflowers.
5. Most people who plant flowers will first decide where they want to plant the flowers. There are many kinds of flower boxes or pots you can build or buy. Gardeners like to plant rows of flowers, too.
6. After picking out the kind of flower and where to plant the flowers, you will need to get materials. Get fresh rich dirt, potting soil and water. If you are planting in the ground, dig a hole for each plant. If you are using a flower box or pot, mix the dirt and soil. Place it in the box or pot and pack it down. Now, for all planting, dig the holes about 2-4 inches deep. Carefully place your flower plant in a hole and pack dirt around it a little higher than the plant bottom. Last, water your plants. Water them to soak in the soil, but not too much to have standing water.
7. Check your plants daily to see if the soil is still damp. Water when it is not damp.
8. Good Luck!

6. What is the main topic of what you read?

Ⓐ How to plant flowers
Ⓑ How to turn seeds into flowers
Ⓒ How to dig gardens
Ⓓ How to buy flower pots or boxes

**7. Paragraph 3 tells you about what is needed in planting flowers.
Use the paragraph to fill in the blanks.**

It is important to plant the flower in the ________________ or it may not grow at all.

________________ need different kind of light to ________________

8. Paragraph 6 tells the steps to planting flowers. Mark yes or no.

	Yes	No
Build flower box		
Dig hole		
Put flower in soil		
Water		

9. The following is paragraph 5. Highlight the main topic sentence.

5.
Most people who plant flowers will first decide where they want to plant the flowers.

There are many kinds of flower boxes or pots you can build or buy.

Gardeners like to plant rows of flowers, too.

10. Write two to three sentences that summarize the passage.

Chapter 2

Lesson 3: Connect the dots

You can scan the QR code given below or use the url to access additional EdSearch resources including videos and mobile apps related to *Connect the dots*.

Connect the dots

URL	QR Code
http://www.lumoslearning.com/a/ri23	

Our First President

Read the story and answer the questions. Read it more than one time to better understand it.

George Washington was the first President of the United States. There are many events that led to this happening. He was born in Virginia on February 22, 1732. Our country was ruled by England. George became a surveyor. This means that he did things like making maps. He was also a farmer. His farm was called Mount Vernon.

George Washington married Martha Custis. She already had 2 children. He helped raise them.

People did not want to be a part of England. They wanted their own country. He joined these people. George was a general in the American Revolutionary Army.

He fought in the Revolutionary War to free America from England. It was a long and hard fight. The colonists won the war.

The new country was named the United States of America.

George Washington was elected as the first President in 1789. He was a good man and very important to our country.

1. How did George Washington help our country? Pick 2 answers.

Ⓐ He became a surveyor.
Ⓑ He fought in the American Revolutionary War.
Ⓒ He got married.
Ⓓ He became the first President of the United States.

2. Who ruled America when George was born? Fill in the blank.

.... ruled America at that time.

3. Put the events in the right order to show how one led to another.

Ⓐ George Washington was important to our country.
Ⓑ George Washington joined the people in a war against England.
Ⓒ He was a general in the American Revolutionary War.
Ⓓ George Washington became President of the United States.

1	
2	
3	
4	

4. Which of the sentences does NOT show how George Washington helped our country?

Ⓐ He lived on a farm named Mount Vernon.
Ⓑ He was important to our country.
Ⓒ He joined the fight against England.
Ⓓ He was President of the United States.

5. What jobs did George Washington have in his life? Pick those that the story talked about.

Ⓐ President of the United States
Ⓑ Surveyor
Ⓒ A general in the Revolutionary War
Ⓓ Farmer

Name: ______________________ Date: ______________

Procedural text

Many times, you must do something you do not know how to do. There are steps you can follow.

What is a "procedural text"?

Procedure text is another way of saying directions, instructions, or guides.

It is a way to do or make something. Steps are given.

You can find recipes for cooking, science experiments, rules for games, or making a project.

You might need to know how to use things like a machine or even a computer.

You can see the steps in little titles under the big title, directions or as a list to follow.

They can have pictures to help, too.

When following "procedural texts", you must go from one step to the other. Do not skip steps.

Here is a procedural text. Read it. Then answer questions.

Cooking Corn Dogs

1. Buy a box of frozen corn dogs.
2. Have an adult turn on the oven to 350 degrees.
3. Spray an aluminum pan with cooking spray.
4. Take the number of corn dogs out that you want to cook.
5. Put them in the pan.
6. Have an adult place the pan in the heated oven.
7. Cook on one side for 12 minutes.
8. Have an adult turn the corn dogs over.
9. Cook on this side for 12 minutes.
10. Have an adult take them out of the oven.

Enjoy! They are best with mustard to dip them in.

6. What does "procedural text" mean? Fill in the blanks from what you read.

Procedure text is another way of saying ______________________________

or ______________

7. Fill in the chart with what would or would not be examples of procedural text.

	Would Be	Would Not Be
Science experiment		
Recipe for cooking		
Computer instructions		
Cartoon		
Candy		

8. Which is the most important thing to remember?

Ⓐ There can be pictures to help you.
Ⓑ Do not skip any steps in following directions.
Ⓒ You do not need steps to follow.
Ⓓ Steps can be in titles, subtitles or a list.

9. In the recipe for corn dogs, who does it say you will need in the steps?

9.1 Why do you think that person is needed? Write your own sentence.

10. What would make the recipe for cooking corn dogs better? Think about the things that can be in a procedural text.

Ⓐ More information about the oven
Ⓑ Chips and dip
Ⓒ Pictures
Ⓓ A book about corn dogs

Chapter 2

Lesson 4: What Does It Mean?

You can scan the QR code given below or use the url to access additional EdSearch resources including videos and mobile apps related to *What Does It Mean?*

What Does It Mean ?

URL	QR Code
http://www.lumoslearning.com/a/ri24	

Read and answer the questions.

Wind

Have you ever heard the wind blowing? Have you looked up in the trees and seen the leaves moving? When air is moved around outside it is called wind. The wind can be stronger than the branches of a tree. Wind can bend the branches up and down and break trees. High winds can be dangerous to people and things. You can even hear wind howling as it moves from one area to another.

1. What is moving air called?

2. What does bend mean in the text?

Ⓐ to run around
Ⓑ to move one way or another
Ⓒ to fix
Ⓓ to change color

Sound

Sound can travel. Sound must have **material** to go through like air, or water. When sound goes through air it is not as fast as if it goes through water. Sound moves 4 times quicker through water.

How fast? Scientists say that sound can go about 767miles an hour when it travels in water.

3. Which two words mean the same in the text? Pick two sets of words.

Ⓐ sound, material
Ⓑ fast, quicker
Ⓒ goes, moves
Ⓓ say, can

4. What examples of material are given in discussing sound?

Name: ______________________ Date: ____________

Solar Wind Turbines

You may have noticed the lines tall white windmills going down a highway or in a field. These are solar wind turbines. They make energy and help to <u>conserve</u> natural resources. This means things like coal, oil, or gas that are found in our soil do not have to be as much. Less of our resources are used up.

The solar wind turbines make electricity. They do this by using the wind to make electricity. The wind turns the huge blades, and the end process is electricity.

5. What is another name for the tall white windmills?

Ⓐ turning blades
Ⓑ natural resources
Ⓒ field electricity
Ⓓ solar wind turbines

6. What does the word <u>conserve</u> mean in this text? Mark the sentences that explain.

Ⓐ These are solar wind turbines.
Ⓑ They make energy and help to conserve natural resources.
Ⓒ This means things like coal, oil, or gas that are found in our soil do not have to be as much. Less of our resources are used up.

7. What is used to make the solar wind turbine blades turn?

Name: ______________________ Date: ______________

The Statue of Liberty

Interesting Facts

1. The real name of the statue is "Liberty Enlightening the World".
2. The statue was given to America is 1886 as a gift from France.
3. The lady represents Libertas, a Roman goddess of freedom. It is a symbol of what she stands for.
4. The statue carries a torch and tablet with the date of the American Declaration of Independence (July 4, 1776).
5. There are 354 stairs to climb to reach the statue's crown.
6. The crown part has 25 windows in it.
7. There are 7 spikes on the crown. They are for the 7 oceans and 7 continents of the world. These show the idea of liberty all over the world.
8. About 4-5 million people visit the Statue of Liberty each year.
9. The statue is made of iron and covered in copper. The copper has turned green due to being exposed to the air.
10. The only way to get to see the statue is by ferry. Boats cannot dock at the island that it is on.

8. What does the word represents mean in #3?

Ⓐ It means that it is the Roman goddess.
Ⓑ It means that it stands for or is a symbol of the Roman goddess.
Ⓒ It means that it looks just like the Roman goddess.
Ⓓ None of these.

9. Think of another word or phrase to use in #4 for carries.

10. What does exposed mean in #9?

Chapter 2

Lesson 5: Special Text Parts

You can practice hyperlink searching, keyword searching and related concepts with the help of the example below

Junk Food

These days junk food is very popular. Junk food is used to describe cheap food containing high levels of calories from sugar or fat with little fiber, protein, vitamins or minerals. Junk food can also refer to high protein food like meat prepared with saturated fat, which some believe may be unhealthy. Some fast food restaurants (restaurants that prepare and serve food very quickly to the customer, usually without waiters or waitresses) supply food considered to be junk food. Despite being labeled as "junk", such foods usually do not pose any immediate health concerns and are generally safe when integrated into a well-balanced diet. However, concerns about the negative health effects resulting from the consumption of a junk food-heavy diet, especially obesity, have resulted in public health awareness campaigns, and restrictions on advertising and sale in several countries.

Assignment: Your teacher has asked you to read this article and explain what tools you would use to get more information about junk food.

You might write this:

I would click on the highlighted words "calories", "sugar" and "fat" with my computer mouse, because these words are in blue and underlined text. This means there is a link to more information about the subject. I would also go the internet and use a search engine like Google to search for information using key words like junk food, calories, sugar, fat, saturated fat, good nutrition and any other key words I could think of.

Name: ______________________ Date: ______________

You can scan the QR code given below or use the url to access additional EdSearch resources including videos and mobile apps related to *Special Text Parts.*

Special Text Parts.

URL	QR Code
http://www.lumoslearning.com/a/ri25	

Name: ________________________ Date: ______________

Read the glossary and the text. Answer the questions.

Community Vocabulary to Know Glossary

Citizen- a person living in a community.

Community- the area in which people live.

Congestion- blocked or slowed.

Rural- a farm or country community.

Store- a place where you buy things you need to live on or want.

Suburb- a community close by a city.

Transportation- ways to get from one place to another such as by bus, car, truck, subway, bicycle, train, or plane.

Urban- a city community where many businesses are located.

Citizens of communities do different things in their daily lives. The people in the urban community travel by many kinds of transportation. They often go from one area of the city to others. Some may take cars and then subways to work. Others hop on buses from their locations.

Those who live in the suburbs may find it more difficult to get into the city. Their time can be taken up by congestion on the freeways or searching for parking downtown. This might make them arrive late for work or meetings.

Rural citizens may not go into the city very often. They might raise their own goods. Farming and ranching are a part of their lives. There are some small stores in these areas. When rural citizens go to urban or suburban areas it will take them much longer to get there. They may have trouble finding their way around as urban communities may change. Most citizens of rural areas like living where there are no large businesses around them. They enjoy the peace and quiet of rural life.

Those living in urban and suburban communities have large stores or malls to go to when buying what they want or need. People living in different communities have different ways of living their daily lives.

Name: ______________________ Date: ______________

1. Match the vocabulary words with their definitions.

	Country living	City living	Close to the city living
Urban			
Rural			
Suburban			

**2. Use the glossary to help you answer the question below:
Why would congestion be a problem for those in the suburbs?**

Ⓐ Congestion would be a problem because it might make them late for their jobs.
Ⓑ Congestion would not be a problem because it would help them get to work faster.
Ⓒ Congestion would be a problem because they could not stop when they wanted to.
Ⓓ Congestion would make it easier for them to listen to the radio.

3. List the forms of transportation found in the glossary.

4. Who is a citizen?

A citizen is

5. Why would citizens living in rural areas like it better than living in urban communities? Mark your answer.

Ⓐ Urban citizens like the peace and quiet.
Ⓑ Rural citizens enjoy the peace and quiet.
Ⓒ Suburban citizens like the congestion.
Ⓓ None of the above.

Better Eating

Read the text and answer the questions. Pay attention to the bold words in the text to help you.

Better Eating

When thinking about eating food, think about trying good fruits and vegetables that do not come from a fast food place or have too much sugar put in them. Fruits and vegetables can help you grow and are good for you. Fresh fruits and vegetables are the best.
Let's look at some things you need to know about.

Good Fruits

Have you ever tried apples, bananas, berries, oranges, pears and avocados?
They have good **nutrients** and **vitamins** to keep you healthy.
They help you grow, keep you strong and can help you learn better.
Fruits can help you from getting sick, too.
Some kids like just one kind of fruit, but it is imperative to eat many kinds of fruits.
The nutrients in fruits have minerals in them that your body needs. They have **Vitamin C, A, B1, B2, and B6**. These vitamins are essential for you.

Good Vegetables

Do you like all vegetables? Probably not. Vegetables give you energy you need. You might want to try vegetables like broccoli, cauliflower, cabbage, greens and of course, green beans, corn and carrots. Some people cook their vegetables while others like them **raw**.
Vegetables have **nutrients** and **vitamins** in them, too.
Nutrients in vegetables give you minerals such as vitamin **A, B7, B9, and K**. Vegetables can help build strong bones and teeth while you grow.

How Much to Eat Each Day?

For your age, you should eat about 1 ½ cups of fruit each day and about 2 cups of vegetables.
Surprise your parents and ask them to make you a chart to be sure you are eating the amount you should each day!
Fruits and vegetables will not make you fat. So, eat plenty! It's ok to eat more, too!

6. In Good Fruits and in Good Vegetables the words nutrients and vitamins are in bold print. How does this help you? Pick 2 answers.

Ⓐ It helps you to look for what the words mean.
Ⓑ It helps you to find examples of nutrients and vitamins.
Ⓒ It helps you read better.
Ⓓ It does not help you.

7. What does the bold word "raw" mean? Write you own answer.

8. Fill in the chart below. Mark those that apply to fruit and to vegetables. They can be in both.

	Fruit	Vegetables
Vitamin A		
Vitamin C		
Vitamin B1		
Vitamin B2		
Vitamin B7		
Vitamin B6		
Vitamin B9		
Vitamin K		

9. What does 'How Much to Eat Each Day' tell you?Mark the best answer.

Ⓐ This section tells you how many cups of fruits to eat each day.
Ⓑ This section tells you how many cups of vegetables to eat each day.
Ⓒ This section tells you how many cups of fruits and vegetables to eat each day.
Ⓓ This section tells you what to tell your parents.

10. What does 'Better Eating' tell you about?

Ⓐ It tells you that what you eat is not important.
Ⓑ It tells you about eating fruits.
Ⓒ It tells you about eating vegetables.
Ⓓ It tells you that fruits and vegetables are good for you.

Chapter 2

Lesson 6: The main purpose of a text

Identify the main purpose of a text, including what the author wants to answer, explain, or describe.

You can scan the QR code given below or use the url to access additional EdSearch resources including videos and mobile apps related to The main purpose of a text.

edSearch ***The main purpose of a text***

URL	QR Code
http://www.lumoslearning.com/a/ri26	

Name: ______________________ Date: ______________

Owls

About Owls

Owls are beautiful! Let's look at their characteristics.

Owls live in many places. Some live in rainforests, deserts, farms, marshes, woods, and on plains. Owls can be seen in other places, too. The Snowy Owl and Hark Owl can stay in very cold weather. They do not like the hot or wet weather.

Owls can make very loud noises. People know that owls can "hoot". Owls can make different sounds. They can shriek, hoot, bark, and even grunt like a pig. If they are upset, the noise can sound like clicking and hissing. Get away if you hear this sound when you are near an owl.

Most owls come out at night. They are nocturnal.

Owls have good eyes and even better hearing. They do not have a sense of smell.

Owls like to eat small prey. Owls fly then swoop down and pick their food up with their claws or beaks. They eat insects, snakes, mice, birds, squirrels, and rabbits depending on the kind of owl.

People have owls for pets, too. It is not easy to have a pet owl. You would need to read up on where to find owls to buy, what to keep them in, how to feed them and train them.

Owls are very interesting and beautiful birds.

1. What is the main idea of this passage?

Ⓐ Owls are nocturnal.
Ⓑ Owls have many characteristics.
Ⓒ Some people have owls as pets.
Ⓓ Owls have good hearing.

2. Fill in the chart to show the characteristics of owls. Mark yes or no.

	Yes	No
Nocturnal		
Can be pets		
Have good sense of smell		
Can make loud noises		

3. What is another word for "characteristic"? Read the words and definitions below and choose one.

Ⓐ Shrieking – loud noises, screaming, yelling
Ⓑ Trait- quality that makes something what it is, sets it apart from other things
Ⓒ Nocturnal- comes out at night, sleeps during the day
Ⓓ Swoops- dives down in a fast way

4. Think about the main idea. Pick 2 answers that are true about owls.

Ⓐ Owls usually come out in daylight.
Ⓑ Owls might sleep during the day.
Ⓒ Owls fly down to get their food.
Ⓓ Owls are not good at seeing or hearing.

5. What is a summary of this passage? Write at least two sentences.

Name: ______________________ Date: ______________

Tunnels

Read and answer the questions.

What About Tunnels?

A tunnel is a long hole that is dug underground. Many animals make tunnels and so do people. Tunnels are made and used for many things.

Animals make and use tunnels. Ants, worms and snakes make little tunnels to live in. They push and move dirt to make their way. Moles, chipmunks, prairie dogs, and rabbits make tunnels. These animals use their front paws or feet to dig their tunnels.

People make tunnels, too. You can make a tunnel in the dirt by digging with a small shovel. Tunnels can be made by digging from one end and then digging from the other end to meet in the middle.

Tunnels are used by people, too. They can be made through rock. Rock tunnels top and bottom are strong because the rock is hard. People build tunnels to go through mountains.

Another kind is the soft ground tunnel. It is made by digging through clay, sand, or wet ground. It will need to have support on all sides, top and bottom. Construction workers use metal to make it sturdy, so it will not fall in.

Some tunnels are made by first building the walls and bottom, then putting dirt over the passageway.

Tunnels take a long time to build. There are different uses for tunnels. Tunnels can be used to carry water from one place to another in water plants. Gas pipelines are also tunnels to carry gas from one area to another. Miners use tunnels to get out coal and other minerals. You can find tunnels in some cities, too. Tunnels are found in subways, and underground walkways. They go under streets, through mountains, and through waterways.

Tunnels are made and used by animals and people for many important reasons.

6. What is the main idea of this passage?

Ⓐ Tunnels can go under cities.
Ⓑ Animals can dig tunnels.
Ⓒ Some tunnels are made through rock.
Ⓓ Tunnels are made and used by animals and people for many important reasons.

Name: ______________________ Date: ______________

7. Which details support the main idea?

Ⓐ Animals make and use tunnels.
Ⓑ Tunnels are used by people, too.
Ⓒ There are different uses for tunnels.
Ⓓ Another kind is the soft ground tunnel.

8. Why was this passage written?

Ⓐ This passage was written to tell you that animals make tunnels.
Ⓑ This passage was written to tell how animals and people make and use tunnels.
Ⓒ This passage was written to tell you that tunnels have tops, sides, and bottoms.
Ⓓ This passage was written to warn you about snakes.

9. List 4 places that you can find tunnels. Read the passage again if you need help.

10. Fill in the blank for the sentence with details. Use the passage to help you.

______________________ use metal to make it sturdy, so it will not fall in.

Chapter 2

Lesson 7: Informational Illustrations

Publisher's Note: the following is an example of how to use this standard when it is assigned to you. The illustration uses a table (but it could have used a chart or graph).

In this example, the teacher lists questions that the student is to answer, and a correct answer shows that the student understands the illustration and the text. If there were not questions given, then the student could either make up questions based on the illustration or explain the meaning of the illustration.

The computer technology teacher in the Deep Canyon school district did a survey of all students in grades 3 through 6 to find out the percentage of time students spend using computer software for three kinds of applications: school work, social media and computer-based games. The results of the survey are shown in the table below.

Percentage of Time Students In The Deep Canyon School District Spend Using Computing Software				
Grade	**School Work %**	**Social Media (Ex. Facebook, Twitter, You Tube, Email) %**	**Comput-er based Games %**	**%**
3	**15**	**70**	**5**	**100**
4	**30**	**60**	**10**	**100**
5	**40**	**50**	**10**	**100**
6	**50**	**35**	**15**	**100**

The students were asked to answer the following questions using the information in the table:

1. The students in which grade spent the most time doing school work?
2. Did time spent using the computer for social media increase, stay the same, or decrease from grade 3 to grade 6?
3. The students in which grade spent the most time playing computer-based games?

Your assignment: Your teacher has asked you to use the information in the table to answer the three questions, and to explain how the information in the table helped you.

Here is an example of what you might write to finish this assignment.

It was easy to answer the first question. All I had to do was look down the School Work column and find the largest number, which was 50%, and look at the first column to see which grade matched the 50%. It was Grade 6. To answer the second question, I looked down the Social Media column and noticed that the numbers in each row were getting smaller, so it was easy to see that social media usage decreased from grades 3 to 6. To answer the third question, I looked down the Computer-based Games column and found the largest number opposite Grade 6, which was the grade spending the largest percentage of time playing computer-based games. The table format was a big help.

You can scan the QR code given below or use the url to access additional EdSearch resources including videos and mobile apps related to Informational illustration

edSearch ***Informational illustration***

URL	QR Code
http://www.lumoslearning.com/a/ri27	

The Pulley- A simple machine

Look at the pictures. Read the information. Answer the question.

A blind in a room

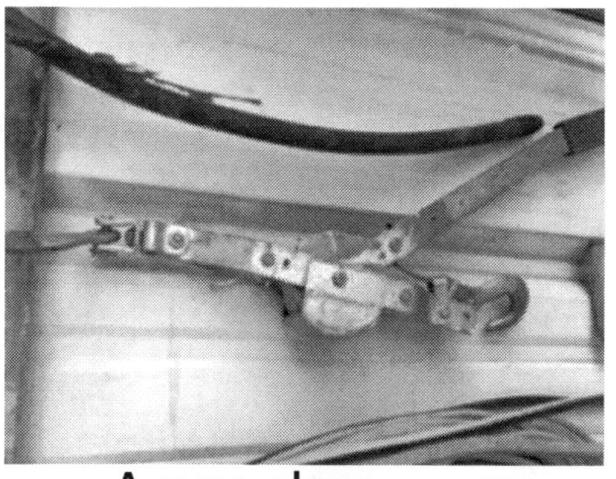

A come-along

A fishing pole

The Pulley- A simple machine

There are many kinds of simple machines. Simple machines make work easier. Pulleys are a kind of simple machine. They can be found in many things we use or see every day. Simple machines do not have a lot of parts. Pulleys are important in making work easier.

Look at the pictures. They all use pulleys. Pulleys come in many sizes. The size depends on the job to be done.

A pulley is a wheel. It is used with a rope, cord, belt or chain. If you pull on the rope, the other end goes up. Pulleys can make things go up and down and pull things. A flagpole runs on a pully. Construction cranes have pulleys. Have you ever seen someone raise a blind to see outside of a window? The blind runs on a pulley. The pictures show a blind in a room, a come-along, and a fishing pole. They all have pulleys.

Each type of pulley has a way to help make the job easier. The string on the blind is connected to the pulley and can raise or lower the blind. The come-along can be attached to a heavy object. By cranking the come-along, the pulley will move the object for you. With a fishing pole, the pulley helps to bring in the fishing line to make it easier to pull in the fish you catch.

Jobs and tasks would be much harder without the use of pulleys. Pulleys help people in many ways.

1. How do the pictures of objects using pulleys help you to understand the text?

Ⓐ The pictures along with the text do not help you at all.
Ⓑ The pictures along with the text show the pulleys working.
Ⓒ The pictures along with the text show you how to take apart pulleys.
Ⓓ The pictures along with the text give you a better understanding of how pulleys work in things.

2. What part of this text helps to clarify the meaning? Mark the best answer.

Ⓐ Pulleys are a kind of simple machine.
Ⓑ They can be found in many things we use or see every day.
Ⓒ Simple machines do not have a lot of parts.
Ⓓ Pulleys are important in making work easier.

3. Match the types of pulleys in the objects to their meaning.

	Helps to bring in your fish	**Helps to raise or lower to see outside**	**Helps to move heavy objects**
Blinds			
Come-along			
Fishing pole			

4. How do the pictures help you? Write your own sentence.

5. The text tells about 2 other types of pulleys to help you understand. What are they? Read the text again and fill in the other objects listed.

Name: _______________ Date: _______________

Parts of an Iron and How It Works

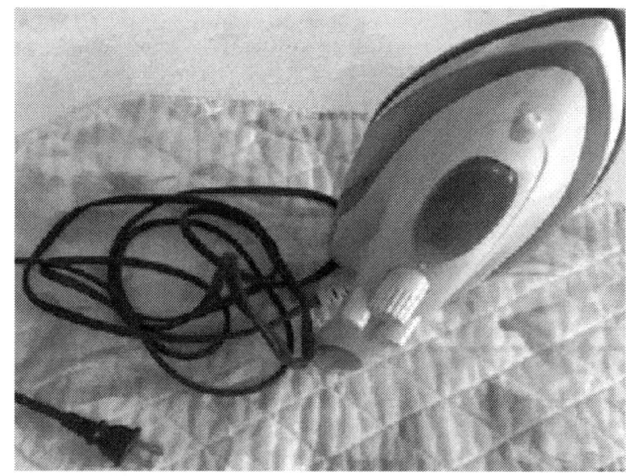

A picture of an Iron

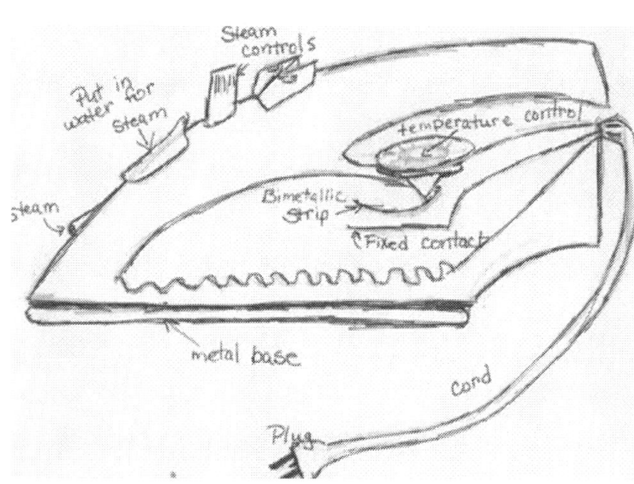

A sketch of an iron with inside parts shown.

Ever see your mom or grandmother use an iron to get wrinkles out of clothes?

An iron is a **machine** that does that. It has a flat metal base. You can use an iron for small or large pieces of clothes or material. The iron is run by electricity. Some irons use steam. The outside of the iron only gets hot on the base at the bottom.

You set the temperature on the control after it is plugged in. The electricity heats up a (metal) **bimetallic strip** making it expand and hit the **fixed contact**, that does not move. This makes the heat.

The iron will get very hot. It is important not to ever touch the base of the iron when it is on or right after using it.

By pressing the iron on the clothes or material and moving it back and forth slowly, wrinkles will go away.

If your iron has a steam **setting**, add water before plugging it in. Then press the steam button when heated and steam will flow out to reduce wrinkles faster.

An iron runs by electricity, heats up and helps get wrinkles out of clothes or material.

6. What do the picture and sketch show? Pick 2 answers.

Ⓐ They show you what an iron looks like.
Ⓑ They show you how to iron clothes.
Ⓒ They show you the inside and outside of an iron.
Ⓓ They show you how not to use an iron.

7. Match the vocabulary words to their definition. Use the text to help you understand the meaning of each.

	A selection, or option	**Something used to get work done**	**Metal that can be heat-ed up**	**Something that does not move**
Machine				
Bimetallic strip				
Setting				
Fixed contact				

8. How do the picture and sketch help you understand important things about an iron and how it works? Pick the best answer.

Ⓐ The picture and sketch tell you how to plug in the iron.
Ⓑ The picture and text give you a better understanding of how an iron works and what it looks like.
Ⓒ The picture and sketch do not match the text.
Ⓓ The iron should not be left on.

9. Which is the best sentence to show and understand the main idea? Use the text and pictures to help you. Mark the best one.

Ⓐ This makes the heat.
Ⓑ The outside of the iron only gets hot on the base at the bottom.
Ⓒ If your iron has a steam setting, add water before plugging it in.
Ⓓ An iron runs by electricity, heats up and helps get wrinkles out of clothes or material.

10. By looking at the picture and sketch and reading the text, what important thing do you need to remember about using an iron?

Ⓐ Ever see your mom or grandmother use an iron to get wrinkles out of clothes?
Ⓑ It is important not to ever touch the base of the iron.
Ⓒ Then press the steam button when heated and steam will flow out to reduce wrinkles faster.
Ⓓ None of these are important.

Name: ______________________ Date: ______________

Chapter 2

Lesson 8: Reason it out

Describe how reasons support specific points the author makes in a text.

You can scan the QR code given below or use the url to access additional EdSearch resources including videos and mobile apps related to Reason it out

edSearch ***Reason it out***

URL	QR Code
http://www.lumoslearning.com/a/ri28	

Signs you need to know

Look at the pictures. Read the text and answer the questions. Reread the text to help you.

Signs to help people

You can see signs everywhere you go. Signs show and tell you about things and places. If you are on a trip, a sign might tell you how far the next town is or where an attraction is located. While in a town or on a street, you see signs for names of stores, businesses, and streets. You need to know that many signs tell us things to do and remember for our safety.

Some signs you know quickly. When you are riding in a car with your parents or others, you might see the stop sign. It is easily recognized. The word stop is in bold and the sign background is red. If you see this sign, be sure to stop. If you are walking look both ways to check to see if anything is coming before you go on.

Another sign that is important in traveling is the buckle up seat belt sign. Many states have this on their highways to remind people that not only it is the law to buckle up, but it is for safety, too. Seat belts keep you from getting hurt in case you are in an accident. Buckle up every time you get in a vehicle.

The third sign shown you might not notice, but it is very important whether you are walking along with a friend or riding in a vehicle. If you see the DANGER sign, it means that you must not go near that place. It might mean that the place or building has chemicals or materials that are harmful. You need to stay away because there is a threat that you could be hurt.

Signs are important in our lives and can help us know where to go, what to do, and what to stay away from, too.

Name: ______________________ Date: ______________

1. What point is the author trying to make in this selection? Mark the best answer.

Ⓐ The point the author is trying to make is that signs are everywhere.
Ⓑ The point the author is trying to make is that signs are important to learn and follow.
Ⓒ The point the author is trying to make is to buckle up.
Ⓓ The point the author is trying to make is that signs are on streets.

2. Fill in the T-chart to show what the reasons are that support the point of the text.

	Danger signs tell you to stay away from something.	**Seat belt signs tell you to put on your seat belt.**	**Stop signs tell you to stop.**
Stop Sign			
Buckle up sign.			
Danger Sign			

3. Which 2 are NOT reasons for following signs?

Ⓐ Signs are hard to figure out.
Ⓑ Only adults need to learn signs.
Ⓒ Signs help keep you safe.
Ⓓ Signs show you what to and what not to do.

4. Using the author's point and reasons, write why signs are important. Reread the text for help.

5. Use the text and fill in the blank to show supporting reasons.

You need to know that many signs tell us ______________________ and

______________________.

Name: ______________________ Date: ______________

What is Our Blue Earth?

Many scientists call the Earth the Blue Earth. Why is this?
Look at a globe or map of the world. See all the blue(dark area). The blue shows what part of the Earth is water. The green(light area) shows what part of the Earth is land.
Think about it. Is the Earth more greenish for land or blue for water?
The Earth is bluer.
The Earth is made up mostly of water.
Water can be found in the oceans, rivers, streams, lakes, creeks, and ponds. It can be in other places, too.
You can find water in both solid and liquid forms on the Earth.
Why can it be in both forms?
Climate is not the same everywhere on the Earth. Weather changes it. That is why some water is a solid and some is liquid. Water can be found as a solid in ice glaciers where it is always cold and below freezing.In warmer areas, water exists as a liquid.
About 72% of the Earth is covered in water. Most of this water is found in the oceans. Animal and plant life can live in it. You cannot drink salt water from the oceans.
Fresh water can be found in rivers, streams, lakes, creeks and pond. You cannot drink all water because it may not be clean. Aquifers are clean water streams found underground.
Water is found in the air, ground, and in animals. It is even in you. You need water to live.
Our Blue Earth is made up of mainly water that can be found in many places and in the form of liquid or solid.

6. What is the point of this text? Mark the best answer.

Ⓐ The point of the text is that the earth has solid and liquid water.
Ⓑ The point of the text is that our earth is blue.
Ⓒ The point of the text is that water is in you.
Ⓓ The point of the text is that our earth is mostly made up of water.

7. Which are supporting reasons of the text? Mark 3 best answers.

Ⓐ 72% of the earth is water.
Ⓑ You cannot drink salt water from the oceans.
Ⓒ A part of the water on Earth is solid, and some liquid.
Ⓓ Water is found in the air, ground, and in animals.

8. Why is this below sentence important? Write your own answer.

Water can be found in the oceans, rivers, streams, lakes, creeks, and ponds. It can be in other places, too.

9. How does the picture of the globe help to support the main point of this article that the earth is mostly water? Fill in the blank.

The globe shows that the earth is mostly water by the color ______________

10. Why is this last sentence in the text that is highlighted important?

Ⓐ It tells the author's main point of the text.
Ⓑ It tells about the earth.
Ⓒ It is not important.
Ⓓ None of these.

Chapter 2

Lesson 9: Compare and contrast

Compare: describe similarities between the two texts in important points and key details.
Contrast: describe the differences between the two texts in important points and key details.

Let us understand the concept with an example.

How to Plan to Present a Theater Play

Here are two different texts on the subject of planning a live theater play.

Text 1: I am Emily, a third grade student. Every year my grade is allowed to put on a show for all the kids in our school. I am so excited! I have been asked to help our theater teacher plan for the play. There are so many things to think about. Here is what I think needs to be done.

First, what kind of show will it be? A comedy, where the actors say and do goofy things to make the audience laugh? Or a drama, where everything is serious? Could it have singing and dancing - a musical comedy or musical drama?

I think a musical would be best. So many of my friends sing in our school chorus, and several take dancing lessons. We would need to ask the kids to buy special dance shoes. We would have to order sheet music for them. We would have to order costumes. We will have to schedule auditions and re-hearsals when kids are available to attend them. But that should not be a problem, since basketball will be over and softball will not have started. And, some of my friends, who do not want to memorize songs or dance steps, can still help by working backstage with props, the curtain, sound and lighting. Oh and I can't wait to see my name in the playbill! Oops, can't forget to write up a playbill.

Text 2: I am Mr. Jones, the theater arts teacher. Every year my theater students are allowed to put on a show. I have to decide what kind of show my students are best at performing: an original variety show, or an existing comedy or drama? With singing and dancing, or only with spoken dialogue (con-versations)? Because time is limited, it has to be an existing show, not an original creation. Because so many students have had dance and singing lessons, and audiences enjoy comedy, I think a musical comedy will be best.

Next, I have to decide which musical comedy to choose. And how much will the script cost? I want to have a large cast, so many students can have a part onstage or backstage. And an orchestra, which will allow even more students to participate. I will need scenery, which I will have to build, and props which I will have to buy or borrow. And costumes which I will have to find talented parents to make

them or money to buy them. Sheet music for each singer and for the orchestra. I will have plan for microphones and lighting, and find students who will run the audio and lights and move the curtains and scenery and props. I will have to schedule auditions and rehearsals. And I need to design the playbill and be sure I include everyone! And all this within the budget I have been given by the principal. I am glad to have Emily helping me. Lots to do – time to get started.

Compare and contrast.

Both Emily and Mr. Jones thought about some of the same tasks needed to plan the play. For example, both chose a musical comedy as the best kind of play. They also knew to include sheet music, costumes, a backstage crew and a playbill.

Mr. Jones also thought of some other tasks. He had concerns about performing the play within a budget, including the costs of the scripts and how to get the costumes made or rented. He thought about the scenery needed, and the need for the orchestra, instead of recorded music. He also realized he would have to give training specific to the play for the students handling lighting, sound, props and scenery.

You can scan the QR code given below or use the url to access additional EdSearch resources including videos and mobile apps related to *Compare and Contrast*.

edSearch ***Compare and Contrast***

URL	QR Code
http://www.lumoslearning.com/a/ri29	

Do You Know Cats? - Facts About Cats

Do You Know Cats?

Cats are very interesting! Many people have them as pets.
Here are a few neat facts you might not know about cats.

1. Cats like to sleep most of the time. (about 12 hours a day)
2. They can jump up to 7x as long as they are.
3. Their tongues are like sandpaper.
4. Cats can make over 100 different kinds of noises.
5. When they put their paws in and out, they are happy.
6. A grown-up cat has 30 teeth.
7. They can jump from high places and still be ok.
8. They say hello to other cats by touching noses.
9. They cannot see if it is totally dark.
10. Cats can run very fast.
11. Their sense of hearing is excellent.
12. Calico cats are usually girl cats.
13. Baby cats are called kittens, grown boy cats are called Toms, and grown girl cats can be called Queens.

Facts about Cats

I read an article on important things we need to know about cats. Here are some of those things.

1. Cats can be sad.
2. Cats cannot see in the dark like some people think. They need to have a little bit of light to see.
3. Cats can hear very well, but not as good as dogs.
4. They have 20 bones in their tails.
5. Cats say hi to each other by touching their noses to each other.
6. Cats can be right or left handed. Most cats do use their right paw more.
7. Cats that live with people usually live to be 12 yrs old.
8. Cats bathe by licking themselves.
9. <u>Domestic</u> cats (those that live with people) love to play.

10. There are about 500 kinds of domestic cats.
11. Kittens are born with blue eyes and then most change colors.
12. Cats have 4 legs, 5 toes on each front paw, only 4 on back paws.
13. They sleep most of the day.

1. What does this article talk mostly about? Mark the best answer that supports it.

Ⓐ Cats sleep most of the time.
Ⓑ Calico cats are usually girl cats.
Ⓒ There are many interesting facts about cats.
Ⓓ Cats can jump high.

2. What sense of hearing do cats have? Mark the best answer.

Ⓐ Their sense of hearing is 7x better than ours.
Ⓑ They have a very good sense of hearing.
Ⓒ They cannot hear very well.
Ⓓ It does not tell about their sense of hearing.

3. List the different names the text says cats can be called.

4. Are cats left or right handed? Write your own sentence. Use a fact from the list to help you.

5. What does domestic mean according to "Facts about Cats?"

Ⓐ Domestic means living in the city.
Ⓑ Domestic means a cat living in the country.
Ⓒ Domestic means 500 kinds of cats.
Ⓓ Domestic means living with people.

6. Fill in the blank using the list.

Cats live to be about ________________ years old.

7. Now look at both texts again. Reread and answer the questions.

Mark the facts that are found in each text. Some may be in both.

	Do You Know Cats?	**Facts about Cats**
Cats sleep a lot.	☐	☐
Cats touch noses to other cats to say hello.	☐	☐
Can't cannot see if it is totally dark.	☐	☐
Cats make over 100 noises.	☐	☐
Cats have 20 bones in their tails.	☐	☐

8. Which facts are found in both?

Ⓐ Cats sleep most of the time.
Ⓑ Cats can hear very well.
Ⓒ Cats touch noses to say hi to each other.
Ⓓ Cats make more than 100 noises.

9. List 4 facts from "Do You Know Cats?" that is not listed in "Facts about Cats".

10. List 4 facts from "Facts about Cats" that is not listed in "Do You Know Cats".

End of Reading: Informational Text

Answer Key and Detailed Explanations

Chapter 2: Reading: Informational Text

Lesson 1: Ask and answer questions

Question No.	Answer	Detailed Explanations
1	C	The third answer is the best answer as it is found in the passage. The other answers are not complete and are not correct.
2	-	The passage states that they are made by people at their **houses**, do not come from a store and are not made in a factory. So, the answers are **houses**, **store**, and **factory**.
3	-	Answers will vary but should include that it is too heavy to move without a trailer and/or that it is put on a trailer to move it around.
4	B	The best answer is the second sentence. It tells the main idea of the passage. It is the correct answer. The first, third, and fourth sentences are not found in the passage.
5	-	The first, third, fourth and fifth uses are found in the passage. They should be marked "yes". The second use should be marked "no". It would not work and cannot be found.
6	mow,plow	This tractor is used to mow, and plow as stated in the passage. These are the only correct answers but can be in either order.
7	A	The first sentence can be found as a detail in the selection. It is the best answer. The others cannot be found and are not correct.
8	-	You would find tractors out in the country, on a farm, or on a ranch. These answers should be marked "yes". You would not find a tractor at a mall. It should be marked "no".
9	-	The story states that he planted corn, tomatoes, potatoes, and peppers. These are the only correct answers.
10	-	Answers will vary but should include that he mows the fields because weeds grow that can make his horses sick if they eat them.

Lesson 2: The Main idea

Question No.	Answer	Detailed Explanations
1	D	The main topic of the article is to give facts about the rainforest. The fourth sentence is correct, the other sentences are details and are not correct.
2	-	The sentence is the main topic sentence of the article. The missing words to be filled in should be "Tropical rainforests". That is the only correct answer.
3	-	1. hibiscus 2. orchard 3. passion flower
4	-	The articles gives examples of snakes both on land and in the water. So that column should be marked for snakes. The others should be marked for land only as the article does not state that these could live in the water.
5	-	The first sentence of this paragraph tells the main topic. It is correct and should be underlined.
6	A	The article's main topic is how to plant flowers. The first answer is correct. The article is not about turning seeds into flowers, how to dig gardens, or how to buy flower pots or boxes. The second, third and fourth sentences are not correct.
7	-	The paragraph states that right light is needed for flowers to grow. Those are the only correct answers.
8	-	The first step is not found and should be marked "no". The second, third and fourth steps are found in paragraph 6 and should be marked "yes".
9	-	The first sentence is the topic sentence. A topic sentence tells the main idea of the paragraph. It is the correct answer.
10	-	Answers will vary. The correct answer should include- The passage is about how to plant flowers. It tells about things you will need to know, materials to get, how to plant the flowers, and water them.

Lesson 3: Connect the dots

Question No.	Answer	Detailed Explanations
1	B, D	The second and fourth sentences show how the events of his life are connected and how he helped our country. They are correct. The second and third sentences are details but do not show how he helped. They are not correct.
2	-	England ruled at that time. It is stated in the second paragraph and is the only correct answer.
3	B, C, D, A	The events that show a connection to history are that George joined the war against England, became a general, President of the United States and was important to our country. This is the correct order for the question.
4	A	The first sentence is a detail in the life of George Washington but does not help you to see how he helped our country. It is the correct answer. The other answers show how he helped and are not correct.
5	A, B, C, D	All of the answers are correct, can be found in the passage, and should be marked.
6	-	The passage states that another way of saying it is directions, instructions or guides and is the only correct answer.
7	-	Science experiments, recipes, and computer instructions are listed as examples of procedural texts in the passage. They should be marked "would be". Cartoons and candy are not and should be marked "would not be".
8	B	The second sentence is the most important and can be found in the passage. It is the correct answer. The first sentence and third sentence are details but not the most important. They are not correct. The third sentence is not in the passage and not correct.
9	-	The recipe says several times that an **adult** is needed. That is the only correct answer.
9.1	-	Answers will vary, but it should state that an adult is needed to make sure the student does not get burned by the hot oven.
10	C	The passage states that pictures can help and that is the only answer that can be found and is correct. The other answers would not help with the recipe.

Lesson 4: What Does It Mean?

Question No.	Answer	Detailed Explanations
1	-	The word "wind" is defined in the text as moving air. It is the correct answer.
2	B	The word "bend" means to move one way or another in the text. The clue is "up and down". The second definition is correct.
3	B, C	The two sets of words that are the same are fast, quicker and goes, moves. The second and third sets are correct. The other sets of words are not the same or similar to each other in meaning. They are not correct.
4	-	The text states that air and water are the materials that sound goes through. Those are the only correct answers.
5	D	The text states that they are solar wind turbines. The fourth answer is correct. The other answers are not.
6	B, C	The last two sentences explain what conserve means in the text. It means to use less.
7	-	The text states that wind makes the blades turn. The word "wind" is the only answer.
8	B	The third fact gives detail that shows "represents" means it is stands for or is a symbol of the Roman goddess. The second answer is correct. The other answers are not correct.
9	-	Answers will vary. Accept all answers that show she either holds, grasps, or has in her hand.
10	-	-

Lesson 5: Special Text Parts

Question No.	Answer	Detailed Explanations
1	-	The glossary gives the definitions. Rural is country living, urban is city living, and suburban is close to the city living. These are the only correct answers.
2	A	The first answer is correct. In the glossary it states that congestion is something blocked or slowed. If the traffic was blocked or slowed down, people could be late for their jobs. The other answers are not found and are not correct.
3	-	The glossary lists bus, car, truck, subway, bicycle, train and plane. These are the correct answers. They may be in any order.
4	-	Answers will vary. The correct answer should say that it is a person who lives in a community. It can give more details such as anyone living in a certain place, a person living in an area, somebody who lives somewhere, etc.
5	B	The second sentence tells why citizens like living in rural communities. They enjoy the peace and quiet. This answer is found in the text and is the only correct answer. The first, third, and fourth answers are incorrect.
6	A, B	The bold words help you to look for the meaning and find examples. The first and second sentences are correct. The third and fourth sentences are not found and are not correct.
7	-	Answers will vary but should state that "raw" means not cooked.
8	-	Vitamins in fruits are A, C, B1, B2 and B6 and should be marked that way. Vitamins in vegetables are A, B7, B9, and K and should be marked that way. These are found in bold print in the text.
9	C	The third answer is the best answer and is correct as it states the main topic of this section. The first, second and fourth answers are not the main topic and are not correct.
10	D	The fourth sentence is correct. It tells the main idea of the first bold print title. The first answer does not follow the text, the second, and third are details and not complete. They are not correct.

Lesson 6: The main purpose of a text

Question No.	Answer	Detailed Explanations
1	B	The main idea is that "Owls have many characteristics". The second sentence is the correct answer. The others are details and not the main idea. They are not correct.
2	-	The characteristics in the passage are nocturnal, can be pets, and can make loud noises. These should be marked "yes". They do not have a good sense of smell. That one should be marked "no".
3	B	Characteristic and trait mean the same thing. The second sentence is correct. The other words and definitions do not match the characteristic definition. They are not correct.
4	B, C	The second and third answers are correct. The first and fourth answers are not true. They are not correct.
5	-	Answers will vary. They should include that owls have many characteristics. Some characteristics that should be included are that owls are nocturnal, swoop down to catch food, eat insects, mice, small animals, make loud noises and can be pets. Accept all answers that include some of these.
6	D	The passage is about how tunnels are made and used by animals and people for many important reasons. The fourth answer is correct. The other answers are details and not the main idea. They are not correct.
7	A, B, C	The first three sentences are details that support the main idea and are correct. The fourth sentence is a detail, but does not support the main of idea of tunnels are made and used by animals and people. It is not correct.
8	B	The second sentence tells why the passage was written. It is correct. The first and third sentences are details but do not tell why the passage was written. The fourth sentence does not pertain to the passage. The first, third and fourth sentences are not correct.
9	-	Answers will vary. These are found in the passage, but others could be listed as noted below and should be marked as correct, too. They can be in any order, too. Additional correct answers: Under streets Subways Underground walkways Gas pipelines
10	-	The passage detail states that construction workers is the correct answer and the only answer.

Lesson 7: Informational Illustrations

Question No.	Answer	Detailed Explanations
1	D	The first, second and third sentences are not found and are not correct. The fourth sentence give the overall main idea, the pictures and text help you to better understand pulleys and is correct.
2	D	The last sentence clarifies the purpose of the text and is correct. The other sentences are details that support the main idea. They are not correct.
3	-	The objects should be matched as to what the pulleys help each one to do. The first object should be fishing pole, as it helps bring in the fish, the second one should be blinds as it helps to raise or lower, and the third one should be come-along as it helps to move heavy objects. These are the only correct answers.
4	-	Answer will vary. The answer should include that they help you to see the objects and then read the text to understand how the pulleys work in each one to make the work easier.
5	-	The text lists a flagpole and construction cranes. These are the only correct answers but may be listed in a different order.
6	A,C	The correct answers are the first and third sentences. The second and fourth sentences cannot be seen in the pictures and are not correct.
7	-	Using context clues from the text, the following answers are found and correct. Setting is a selection or option, machine is something used to get work done, bimetallic strip is a metal that can be heated up, and a fixed contact is something that does not move. These are the only correct order for the answers.
8	B	The best answer is the second one as it gives the main idea of the text and how the picture and sketch help you to understand. It is correct. The first, third, and fourth answers do not give an understanding of the text. They are not correct.
9	D	The fourth answer is the best sentence to show and understand the main idea. It is the correct answer. The first, second and third answers are details and not correct.
10	B	The second sentence is correct because it shows that you should never touch the base of the iron when it is on. The other sentences do not tell you important things to remember and are not correct.

Lesson 8: Reason it out

Question No.	Answer	Detailed Explanations
1	B	The second sentence is the point that the author is trying to make. It is correct because it states in the text that signs are important to learn and follow to help you and keep you safe. The first, third, and fourth sentences are details but not the topic. They are not correct.
2	-	The signs are listed as stop sign first, telling you to stop; buckle up sign second, telling you to put on your seat belt; and third danger sign, telling you to stay away from something. These are the only correct answers and correct order.
3	A, B	The first and second sentences are NOT reasons for following signs and are correct. The third and fourth sentences are reasons and are not correct.
4	-	Answers will vary but need to include that signs are important to help keep you safe. The reasons given are to follow stop signs, follow buckle up signs, and danger keep out signs for your safety. Accept all reasonable answers.
5	-	The sentence is taken directly from the text. The only correct answers are "things to do" and "remember for our safety".
6	D	The fourth sentence tells the main point of the text. The earth is made up mostly of water. The first and third sentences are details that support the point but are not the point and not correct. The second sentence is false and not correct.
7	A, C, D	The first, third and fourth sentences support the main point, 72% of the earth is water, some water is a solid and some is liquid, water is found in the air, ground and in animals. They are correct. The second sentence does not support the main point and is not correct.
8	-	Answers will vary but should include that this gives details to all the places where water can be found on the earth. This supports the point that the earth is mostly water.
9	-	The globe shows water by the color blue(dark area) and blue is the only correct answer.
10	A	The first sentence- It tells the author's main point of the text- is correct. Our Blue Earth is made up of mainly water that can be found in many places and in the form of liquid or solid. The second answer is not the main point, and the third and fourth answers are not found. These are not correct.

Lesson 9: Compare and contrast

Question No.	Answer	Detailed Explanations
1	C	The third sentence is the best answer as it tells how the reasons support what the author is trying to tell about. The first, second and fourth answers are details. They are not correct.
2	B	The text says that cats have excellent hearing. The second sentence is correct. The other sentences are not correct and not found.
3	-	The text says that cats are called kittens when they are babies, grown boy cats are called Toms and grown girl cats are called Queens. These are the only correct answers but can be in any order.
4	-	Answers will vary but should include that cats can be either left or right handed and most use their right paws.
5	D	The fourth sentence is explained in #9 Cat Facts as living with people for the definition of domestic. It is the only correct answers. The others are not correct and not stated as the definition.
6	-	This is the only correct answer that is stated in the text. 12 years old.
7	-	**Facts found in Both:** • Cats sleep a lot. • Cats touch noses to other cats to say hello. • Can't cannot see if it is totally dark. **Facts found only in Do You Know Cats?** • Cats make over 100 noises. **Facts found only in Cat Facts?** • Cats have 20 bones in their tails.
8	A, B, C	The first three sentences are correct as these facts are in both texts. The fourth sentence is not correct as it is only in one text.

Question No.	Answer	Detailed Explanations
9	-	• They can jump up to 7x as long as they are. • Their tongues are like sandpaper. • Cats can make over 100 different kinds of noises. • When they put their paws in and out, they are happy. • A grown-up cat has 30 teeth. • Cats can run very fast. • Calico cats are usually girl cats • Baby cats are called kittens, grown boy cats are called Toms, and grown girl cats can be called Queens. **The answers listed are only found in Do You Know Cats? The student must have 4 of them to be correct and may be in any order for credit.**
10	-	• Cats can be sad. • They have 20 bones in their tails. • Cats can be right or left handed. Most cats do use their right paw more. • Cats that live with people usually live to be 12 yrs old. • Cats take baths by licking themselves. • Domestic cats (those that live with people) love to play. • There are about 500 kinds of domestic cats. • Kittens are born with blue eyes and then most change colors. • Cats have 4 legs, 5 toes on each front paw and only 4 on back paws. **The answers listed are only found in CAT FACTS. The student must have 4 of them to be correct and may be in any order for credit.**

Chapter 3
Reading Foundational skills

The Objective of the Reading Foundational Skills standards is to ensure that students understand and have working knowledge of concepts of print, the alphabetical principle, and other basic conventions of the English Writing system.

To help master the necessary skills, we encourage the student to go through the resources available online on EdSearch to gain an in depth understanding of these concepts. The EdSearch page for each lesson can be accessed with the help of the url or the QR code provided.

Chapter 3

Lesson 1 : Decode the words

You can scan the QR code given below or use the url to access additional EdSearch resources including videos and mobile apps related to *Decode the words*.

Decode the words

URL	QR Code
http://www.lumoslearning.com/a/rf23	

Name: ______________________ Date: ______________

1. **Read the list of words below. When we look at words, we can put them in order of the alphabet to help understand and read them. This list can be done by the first letter. Write the words in the correct ABC order.**

Ⓐ banana
Ⓑ drive
Ⓒ apple
Ⓓ carrot
Ⓔ elephant

1	
2	
3	
4	
5	

2. **We can also sort words by their second letter if the first letter is the same. Look at the list below. Mark the long vowel word that is NOT in the correct ABC order.**

Ⓐ Tail
Ⓑ Train
Ⓒ Team
Ⓓ Tone

3. **When 2 vowels are together in a word, the first vowel is usually long and the second one silent. Read the list of words in the box and mark which has a short vowel sound, and which has a long vowel sound.**

	Short vowel sound	**Long vowel sound**
Mail		
Street		
Bat		
Box		

4. **Read the words below and write the vowel combination for each.**

	Vowel Combination
sneak	
goat	
trail	
clean	
deep	

5. **Choose the following 2 syllable long vowel words to complete the sentences below. Fill in the blank.**

(explain, mailbox, basement)

a. **She ran to check the ______________________ to see if her package came.**

b. **His brother plays pool in the ______________________ with his friends.**

c. **They had to ___________________ to their parents why they were late for dinner.**

6. **Read the words below and decide if they have a suffix or prefix added. Mark it in the box.**

	Prefix	**Suffix**
playing		
misbehave		
sickly		
reread		

7. **The words below are compound words. A compound word is two little words put together to make a bigger word with a different meaning. Read the words and separate the two words.**

Compound Word	First word	Second word
playground		
mailbox		
outdoor		
birthday		

8. **Use what you know and decode the words below in the sentences. Mark the sentence that makes sense and uses the right verb.**

Ⓐ We playing a long time today with our friends.
Ⓑ We have been playing a long time today with our friends.
Ⓒ We plays a long time today with our friends.
Ⓓ We is playing a long time today with our friends.

9. **Write your own sentence using the long vowel word below. Then underline the vowel team in the word.**

10. **In words with tch, the t is silent. Read the words below and find the words with tch. Mark those words.**

Ⓐ Math
Ⓑ Match
Ⓒ Watch
Ⓓ What
Ⓔ Finch
Ⓕ Flash

Name: ______________________ Date: ______________

Chapter 3

Lesson 2 :Comprehend the text

You can scan the QR code given below or use the url to access additional EdSearch resources including videos and mobile apps related to *Comprehend the text*

Comprehend the text

URL	QR Code
http://www.lumoslearning.com/a/rf24	

Giraffes Are Cool

A giraffe is a very tall animal. They can be found in the wild in Africa. Many zoos have giraffes, too. When we think of or picture a giraffe, we see the long, long neck. They are extremely tall. It would take at about 3 humans to be as tall as a giraffe. By being this tall, they can keep a close eye out for any animals that could hurt them, like hyenas or lions.

They weigh over 2 thousand pounds and can run about 35 miles an hour.
A funny thing is that the male is called a bull and the female is called a cow.

Giraffes are plant eating animals. They eat leaves and tiny branches called twigs. Giraffes do not drink much water. The reason for this is that they get most of their water from the leaves they eat. 75% of the time, giraffes are eating or roaming around. They even sleep standing up.

They like to stay together in large groups. There can be nearly 15 or so in a group. In the wild, they live to be around 25 years old, but in the zoos, they can live to be nearly 40.

1. Which 3 of the following are facts about giraffes that you read in the story?

Ⓐ Giraffes weigh over 2 thousand pounds.
Ⓑ Giraffes sleep most of the day.
Ⓒ Giraffes sleep standing up.
Ⓓ Giraffes can be found in the wild in Africa.

2. Find the correct sentence about how fast giraffes can run. Mark your answer.

Ⓐ They can run over 75 miles an hour.
Ⓑ They can run about 35 miles an hour.
Ⓒ They do not run, they jump.
Ⓓ They run about 10 miles an hour.

3. Why don't giraffes drink a lot of water like other animals? Write your own sentence.

4. Look at the chart. Mark if the detail is or is not a fact about giraffes.

	Is a fact	Is not a fact
Giraffes eat mice.		
Giraffes can be 3 times taller than people.		
Giraffes are only found in Africa.		
Males are called bulls and females are called cows.		

5. What do you think is the best reason that giraffes live longer in zoos than in the wild? Mark your answer.

Ⓐ Giraffes live longer at zoos because kids can go see them.
Ⓑ Giraffes live longer at zoos because they get more water in zoos.
Ⓒ Giraffes live longer at zoos because they are not bothered or eaten by hyenas or lions.
Ⓓ Giraffes live longer in the wild, not in zoos.

Christopher Columbus

Christopher Columbus was born in Italy in 1451. He worked on ships as a teenager. Columbus was interested in exploring the world and studied geography.

When he was about 35 he met the King and Queen of Spain. He told them he wanted to find a quicker way to the trade countries to get spices and gold. They gave him 3 ships and money. The names of the ships were the Nina, Pinta, and Santa Maria.

Columbus hired many sailors to go with him. They sailed until they saw land. He thought he had gone around the world. He had not. In the New World, he found natives and traded with them.

He sailed back to Spain. He brought back many things from the New World, including some of the natives. The king and queen were happy with his finds. Columbus sailed several more times.

In the United States, we celebrate Columbus Day each year in October.

6. Where was Columbus born? Reread to find out.

7. Why did the King and Queen of Spain give Columbus three ships? Choose the best answer.

Ⓐ They wanted him to be famous.
Ⓑ They wanted him to find the natives.
Ⓒ They wanted him to find a quicker way to trade for spices and gold.
Ⓓ They liked him very much.

8. The story tells what Columbus did as a teenager and before he made his journey. What 3 things did it say he did? Mark the answers.

Ⓐ Playing sports
Ⓑ Studying geography
Ⓒ Interested in exploring the world
Ⓓ Working on ships

9. Did Columbus really find a new way to the trade countries?Write your answer as "yes" or "no"

10. What did Columbus think he had done? Mark the best answer.

Ⓐ He thought he had gone around the world.
Ⓑ He thought he had made it back to Spain.
Ⓒ He thought he was in the United States.
Ⓓ He thought he was rich.

Chapter 3

Lesson 3 : Understand the purpose of the text

edSearch *Understand the purpose of the text*

URL	QR Code
http://www.lumoslearning.com/a/rf24a	

Benjamin Franklin

Did you know that Benjamin Franklin was not only an inventor, but a scientist, soldier, politician, post-master, and author?

Benjamin Franklin was born in Boston, Massachusetts on January 17, 1706. He lived for 84 years.

Franklin was one of our country's "Founding Fathers". He signed the Declaration of Independence, the Treaty of Paris and the U.S. Constitution.

He is well known for his experiment with electricity, the kite and key with lightning during a thunder-storm. Franklin invented glasses called bifocals, too. Some of your grandparents may even have or remember his invention called the Franklin stove.

One of his famous writings is Poor Richard's Almanac. It was written years ago and is still published and bought today. In this book, he gives facts about weather, and recipes. He wrote funny sayings and jokes in his works, too.

Name: ______________________ Date: ____________

1. What did you learn from reading this story? Mark those that apply.

Ⓐ Benjamin Franklin was a Founding Father of our country.
Ⓑ Benjamin Franklin was an author and wrote Poor Richard's Almanac.
Ⓒ Benjamin Franklin was a skinny man with glasses.
Ⓓ He invented bifocals and the Franklin stove.

2. Fill in the words below to complete the sentences about Mr. Franklin.

U.S. Constitution
84
Founding Fathers
electricity

a. Franklin did experiments with a key, and kite during a thunderstorm to show

______________________ .

b. Benjamin Franklin is one of our country's ______________________ .

c. He lived to be __________ years old.

d. Mr. Franklin signed the Declaration of Independence, the Treaty of Paris and the

______________________ .

3. List the 6 jobs that Mr. Franklin held as stated in the story.

Name: ______________________ Date: ______________

4. What do you think the purpose of this text is? Write your own sentence.

5. Mark if the sentences are true or false about Benjamin Franklin.

	True	False
He was an inventor		
He was not a soldier		
He helped our country		
He is not known for anything except experiments on electricity.		

Susan B.Anthony

Susan B.Anthony was born in 1820. She was from a large Quaker family. Quakers are a kind of religious group that believes in rights for all. They lived on a farm. She had many brothers and sisters.

Her farm was a meeting place for people against slavery. They believed in equal rights for all. The abolitionists such as Frederick Douglas came to the meetings.

She started teaching at the age of 17.

Susan B.Anthony started a movement to help women gain the right to vote. She spoke around the country for freedom for slaves and women's rights.

She started the Women's Suffrage movement and an organization to help women.

She did not believe that men should have the right to vote when women did not.

After she died, the 19th Amendment was passed giving women the right to vote.

Later in 1979, a silver dollar was made and distributed with her picture on it.

She is well remembered for her work in civil rights.

6. Which of the following sentences tell why she started the Woman's Suffrage movement?

Ⓐ Men were getting less money than women.
Ⓑ Women were not able to vote.
Ⓒ She was a Quaker.
Ⓓ They had meetings on her parent's farm.

7. What is the purpose- reason why this text was written? Write your own sentence.

8. What happened after she died? Mark 2 sentences that give details.

Ⓐ She became a teacher at the age of 17.
Ⓑ The 19th Amendment was passed that gives women the right to vote.
Ⓒ In 1979 a silver dollar was made to honor her.
Ⓓ She had 6 brothers and sisters.

9. Choose the correct definition for the word- abolitionists.

Ⓐ A religious group living on a farm.
Ⓑ People against slavery who believed in equal rights for all.
Ⓒ People wanting women to vote.
Ⓓ People who make silver dollars.

10. Choose the details that helped you learn more about Susan B. Anthony.

Ⓐ She was born into a Quaker family that believed in equal rights for all.
Ⓑ She was against slavery.
Ⓒ Susan B Anthony started a group for women's rights including the right to vote.
Ⓓ She is well remembered for her work in the civil rights.

Name: ______________________ Date: ______________

Chapter 3

Lesson 4 : Use context to find the meaning of words

You can scan the QR code given below or use the url to access additional EdSearch resources including videos and mobile apps related to *Use context to find the meaning of words*

edSearch ***Use context to find the meaning of words***

URL	QR Code
http://www.lumoslearning.com/a/rf24c	

Read the text below. Reread it at least three times to help you. The words in bold may be new words for you. To use context clues in a text, it is important to read all the sentences around the new word. This will help you understand the meaning of the new words. After you have read the text many times, use what you learn to answer the questions about the new vocabulary.

Climate Change

Regional temperatures are changing with the climate. This change in certain areas of the country makes it hard for plants and animals to live. Animals may need to **relocate** to places that have the temperatures they are used to living in. This move can be difficult for them.

This change may cause some **species** to move father north where the weather is cooler or farther south where the weather is warmer. Many kinds of animals migrate each year and more are doing so with the climate changes.

With the changes in climate, there may be different places in which plants can still grow in certain areas. The land and water are also affected. Researchers use **data** to help them understand these changes. Reports, charts, graphs, and daily monitoring of land is detailed in the information gathered.

Currents in the oceans have impact on the climate changes, too. The speed and direction of the water moving on the ocean floor is being studied to help add more information.

Scientists hope this research will help them understand more about climate change.

1. Which is the best definition of the word "Regional"?

Ⓐ Cities in the country
Ⓑ Certain areas of the country
Ⓒ A way to get data for the scientists
Ⓓ Climate change

Name: ______________________ Date: ____________

2. Why do animals relocate? Write a sentence that explains.

3. In understanding the word "species" what words help you? Highlight the set of under lined words that help you.

This change may cause some species to move father north where the weather is cooler or farther south where the weather is warmer. Many kinds of animals migrate each year and more are doing so with the climate changes.

4. List what scientists use in their "data".

5. Which is NOT the meaning of "currents" in this passage? Mark the best answer.

Ⓐ Moving waters
Ⓑ Direction and movement of ocean waters
Ⓒ Flowing waters
Ⓓ Water that is not moving

Name: ______________________ Date: ____________

Mr. Green's Class

Read the text below. Reread it at least three times to help you. The words in Bold may be new words for you. To use context clues in a text, it is important to read all the sentences around the new word. This will help you understand the meaning of the new words. After you have read the text many times, use what you learn to answer the questions about the new vocabulary.

Students were not sure about Mr. Green on the first day of school. Some of the third graders said that he was **cruel** to them when they had him as a teacher.

Pupils were a little scared when they heard he was their teacher. He was reported to be harsh in his tone of voice and mean to them when they asked for help.

They were so surprised to find out that he was very nice. He did have rules they had to follow each day. If the students followed the rules, he gave them **rewards**. This could be stickers, free time on the computer, game time and extra recess time.

Mr. Green's pupils were no longer afraid. He was **not selfish** at all. He took time to listen to them and **allowed** students choices in their work. He would let them pick some of their assignments. Mr. Green was caring and kind. He did what was best for his class.

The students told the third graders that they were wrong about him. The third graders laughed and said they knew he was a good teacher. They said they had played a joke on them.

6. What does the word cruel mean in the story?

- Ⓐ dirty or oily
- Ⓑ mean and harsh
- Ⓒ happy and funny
- Ⓓ none of the above

7. Read the paragraph and round which 3 sets of underlined words help you to know what the words not selfish mean.

Mr. Green's pupils were <u>no longer afraid</u>. He was not selfish at all. He <u>took time to listen</u> to them and <u>allowed students choices</u> in their work. He would let them pick some of their assignments. Mr. Green was <u>caring and kind</u>. He did what was best for his class.

8. List the kinds of rewards that Mr. Green gives his class.

9. What does the word allowed mean in the story? Mark the best answer.

Ⓐ does not happen
Ⓑ let something happen
Ⓒ stops something
Ⓓ does not care

10. Context clues help you to learn new words. What do you think the word pupils means in the story? Find a word that means the same thing in the story as pupil and write that word.

End of Reading: Foundational Skills

Answer Key and Detailed Explanations

Chapter 3: Reading: Foundational Skills

Name: ______________________ Date: ______________

Lesson 1: Decode the words

Question No.	Answer	Detailed Explanations
1	-	The words should be put in the order of their first letter. The correct answers are apple, banana, carrot, drive, elephant.
2	B	The correct ABC order of these long vowel words would be tail, team, tone, and train. This makes train NOT in the correct order on this list and is the correct answer.
3	-	Following the rule of 2 vowels next to each other, the words mail and street have long vowel sounds. They should be marked long vowel. The words bat and box have only one vowel and have the short vowel sound. They should be marked short vowel.
4	-	The vowel combinations in each word are as follows and are the only correct answers. Sneak-ea, goat-oa, trail-ai, clean-ea, and deep-ee.
5	-	The only correct answers that make sense for each sentence are sentence a. mailbox b. basement c. explain.
6	-	A prefix is found added to the beginning of a word. The words in the list with prefixes are misbehave- mis and reread-re. The words with suffixes are playing-ing and sickly- ly.
7	-	The compound word separations should be play, ground for playground, mail, box for mailbox, out, door for outdoor, and birth, day for birthday. These are the only correct answers and order for answers.
8	B	The only correct answer is the second sentence. We have been playing a long time today with our friends. The other answers do not make sense and are not correct.
9	-	Answers will vary but should include painting in the sentence and ai should be underlined to be correct.
10	B, C	The words in the list with tch are match, and watch. These are the only correct answers and should be highlighted.

Name: ______________________ Date: ______________

Lesson 2: Comprehend the text

Question No.	Answer	Detailed Explanations
1	A, C, D	The first, third and fourth sentences are found in the story. Giraffes weigh over 2 thousand pounds, they sleep standing up, and can be found in the wild in Africa. These are correct and should be marked. The second sentence is not a fact and is not correct.
2	B	The story states that they can run about 35 miles an hour. The second sentence is correct.
3	-	Answers will vary but should include that giraffes get their water from the leaves they eat. That is why they do not need to drink much water.
4	-	Facts- giraffes can be 3 times taller than people, and males are called bulls, females are called cows. Not facts giraffes eat mice, and they are only found in Africa. These are the way the details should be marked to be correct as found in the story.
5	C	The best answer would be that "Giraffes live longer at zoos because they are not bothered or eaten by hyenas or lions." The other answers are not found or related to the passage.
6	-	He was born in Italy as stated in the story. That is the only correct answer.
7	C	The correct answer is the third sentence, "They wanted him to find a quicker way to trade for spices and gold." The other answers are not found and are not correct.
8	B, C, D	The correct answers are studying geography, becoming an explorer, and working on ships. They are the only correct answers and should be marked.
9	No	-
10	A	The story states that he thought he had sailed around the world. The first answer is the only correct answer.

Lesson 3: Understand the purpose of the text

Question No.	Answer	Detailed Explanations
1	A, B, D	Benjamin Franklin was a Founding Father, author and inventor. The first, second and fourth sentences are found in the selection. They are correct. The third sentence is not and is not correct.
2	-	The correct answers are a. electricity b. Founding Fathers c. 84 d. US Constitution These must be in this order and are the only correct answers found in the text.
3	-	Mr. Franklin was an inventor, scientist, soldier, politician, postmaster, and author. These are the jobs listed in the story but can be in any order.
4	-	Answers will vary but should include that the text about Benjamin Franklin was written to help you learn more about what all he did and how he did things to help the country.
5	-	The sentences should be marked true about him being and inventor-the first sentence, and he helped our country-the third sentence. The second sentence and fourth sentence are false and should be marked that way.
6	B	The correct answer is the second sentence- Women were not able to vote. The first sentence is not found and not correct. The third and fourth sentences are details and do not tell why she started the movement. They are not correct.
7	-	Answers will vary but should include that the text was written to show what Susan B. Anthony did in her life to help groups such as slaves, and women.
8	B,C	The first and fourth sentences are not correct as they happened when she was alive. The second and fourth sentences are correct as they happened after her death.
9	B	The word abolitionists means people who are against slavery. The definition is given within the text. This is the only correct answer.
10	A,B,C,D	All of the answers are correct. They should all be marked. She was born into a family that believed in equal rights, she was against slavery, she started a women's rights' group and she is well remember for her work.

Name: ______________________ Date: ______________

Lesson 4: Use context to find the meaning of words

Question No.	Answer	Detailed Explanations
1	B	The best definition is the second choice, certain areas of the country. The other answers do not define the word regional.
2	-	Answers vary but should include that animals relocate- move to find a place that has the temperature climate the same that they are used to living in.
3	-	The words in the paragraph that help you to understand the word "species" that should b underlined are Many kinds of animals. The other underlined words do not tell about or give you clues for the underlined words.
4	-	The text states that scientists use reports, charts, graphs, and daily monitoring of land in their data. These can be in any order, must be listed to be correct.
5	D	The word current in the passage means moving waters, direction and movement of ocean waters, flowing waters. These answers are not correct as the question asks which is NOT the meaning. The fourth sentence is the correct answer- Water that is not moving.
6	B	The word cruel means mean and harsh in the story. The second definition is correct. It does not mean dirty or oily, happy and funny or none of the above. The first, third and fourth answers are not correct.
7	-	The 3 phrases that help you to know what not selfish means are took time to listen, allowed students choices, and caring and kind. These are correct and should be rounded. The first set of underlined words (no longer afraid) does not explain not selfish and is not correct.
8	-	The kinds of rewards that Mr. Green gives his class are stickers, free time on the computer, game time and extra recess time. These are the only correct answers but may be in any order.
9	B	The best answer is the second definition for allowed- let something happen. The other answers are not correct for the word allowed.
10	-	Answers may vary in word choice, but the word pupils in the story means students and this is the correct answer.

Chapter 4 - Language

The objective of the Language standards is to ensure that the student is able to accurately use grade appropriate general academic and domain specific words and phrases related to Grade 2.

To help students to master the necessary skills, we encourage the student to go through the resources available online on EdSearch to gain an in depth understanding of these concepts. The EdSearch page for each lesson can be accessed with the help of the url or the QR code provided.

Chapter 4

Lesson 1: People, Places and Things

You can scan the QR code given below or use the url to access additional EdSearch resources including videos and mobile apps related to *People, Places and Things*.

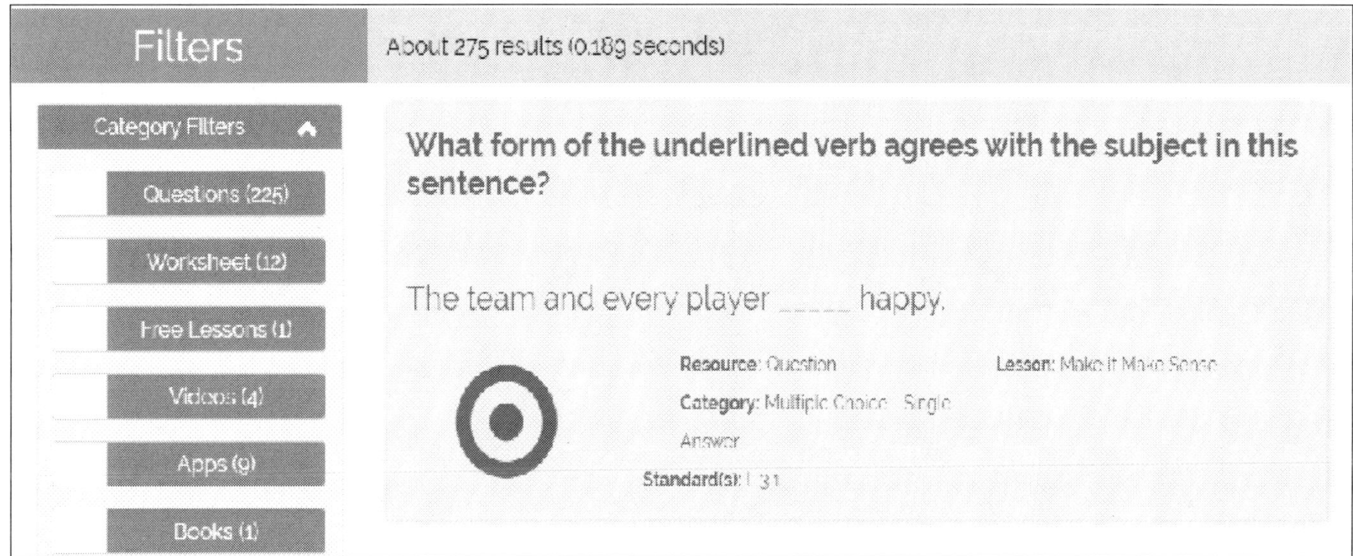

Name: ______________________ Date: ______________

1. **Collective nouns show a group of things. Read the sentences below and choose the collective noun in each sentence. Underline the collective noun.**

We saw a flock of geese in the sky.

Mama said that our cat had a litter of kittens.

Buzzing around us was a swarm of bees.

The pack of wolves howled in the night.

2. **Read the list of collective nouns and choose the right one for each group to describe it.**

flock

bunch

swarm

herd

Group	Collective Noun
cows	
bananas	
birds	
flies	

3. **Mark the sentences that have collective nouns in them.**

Ⓐ We looked for the deck of cards.
Ⓑ Sara picked up the wash.
Ⓒ The children were playing on the playground.
Ⓓ There was a colony of ants in our garden.

4. Which of the following phrases does NOT have a collective noun in it? Mark your answer.

Ⓐ ran to the store
Ⓑ band of soldiers
Ⓒ bundle of papers
Ⓓ bunch of grapes

5. Which collective noun makes sense in the sentence?

Joshua carried a __________ of firewood to the house.

Ⓐ band
Ⓑ swarm
Ⓒ flock
Ⓓ bundle

6. Unscramble the collective nouns and write them correctly.

srwam	
drpie	
fcklo	
nycolo	

7. Choose the correct collective nouns to finish the sentences in the paragraph.
(school, pod, bouquet)

Daddy bought Mom a ______________ of flowers for her birthday. We went to the ocean that day. There was a ______________ of whales swimming far out near a reef. Close-up we also saw a ______________ of fish.

8. Match the words with the best example for the collective nouns.

	pride	bundle	herd	litter
sticks				
puppies				
lions				
buffalo				

9. Mark the 3 sentences below that have collective nouns in them.

Ⓐ Maryann was excited to see the herd of buffalos at Yellowstone National Park.
Ⓑ The students did not see the new teacher quietly enter the room.
Ⓒ The band of soldiers fought hard in the battle.
Ⓓ He could not believe the swarm of bees that came out of the hive.

9.1 Write the collective noun from each sentence in Part A.

10. In thinking about the collective nouns in the questions before, write a sentence that uses the collective noun relating to kittens or puppies.

Name: ______________________ Date: ______________

Chapter 4

Lesson 2: Language conventions

You can scan the QR code given below or use the url to access additional EdSearch resources including videos and mobile apps related to *Language conventions*.

language conventions

URL	QR Code
http://www.lumoslearning.com/a/l12	

Name: ______________________ Date: ____________ 

1. Read the words below and mark the right boxes.

little elephant

really walking

quickly running

fuzzy slipper

	Noun	Adjective	Verb	Adverb
little				
elephant				
really				
walking				
quickly				
running				
fuzzy				
slipper				

2. Read each group of words below. A complete sentence must have a subject and predicate. The subject has the noun in it. The predicate has the verb in it. Mark the 2 sentences that are complete and make sense.

Ⓐ Fishing near the lake.
Ⓑ Margie and I love to go hiking in the woods.
Ⓒ Tracy is happy that he has a new little baby brother.
Ⓓ Skipping down the sidewalk while it is raining.

Name: ______________________ Date: ______________

3. Read the phrase below. Decide what part of the sentence is missing. Write your answers in the blank. The sentence is missing a subject or predicate.

ran a long way home	
My friends and I	
Grandma and Grandpa	
skipping in the rain	

4. Write the right verb for each sentence below. Be careful, each word can only be used one time.

(ran, follow, bake, see, draw)

a. We like to ______________ pictures in Art Class.

b. She would not ______________ the directions the teacher told us.

c. I ______________ all the way home when I was late for dinner.

d. Grandma will ______________ my favorite birthday cake!

e. Did you ______________ her look of surprise?

5. Conjunctions are words used to join 2 simple sentences into 1 compound sentence. Ex ample: 2 simple sentences- John likes baseball. He is the pitcher on the team. Joined: John likes baseball and he is the pitcher on the team. Remember to change the capital letter in the second sentence to lower case when you add the word "and".
Read the sentences below. Using the conjunction "and" make a compound sentence.

Jamar had a party. All his friends came to it.

6. The following is a list of pronouns. A pronoun is a word that takes the place of someone or a proper noun. The pronouns used in a subject are I, you, he, she, they, we, it. Read the sentences below and Underline the subject pronouns.

She liked to visit her Grandpa on the farm.

It was a cloudy and windy day.

He knew the rain was coming soon.

You need to learn how to do your best job.

I am pleased with the work that was done.

We are not going fishing today.

They will be coming over soon.

7. Pronouns can be used in other parts of a sentence to show the object. (They act as objects and receive the action of the in the sentence.) Here are some object pronouns- you, us, them, it, me, him, and her.

Highlight the object pronouns in each sentence.

The girls like her as a singer.

Mom said it was time for us to go to the zoo.

Bobby gave a Ninja puzzle to him for a birthday present.

8. Read the sentences below. Place the subject and predicates in the right boxes. Remember that the subject has a noun in it and the predicate has the verb in it. Write the complete ones for each sentence.

The older man made a funny face.
Skippy was the best puppy I ever had.
Mel and Tom are great friends.
Valerie will be 8 years old in 2 weeks.

Subject	Predicate

9. Find the adjective in each sentence and underline them. Remember an adjective describes or tells more about a noun.

The beautiful princess lived in a castle.

The curious kitten played with the yarn all day.

She was a shy girl.

Sam loved to eat and had a healthy appetite.

10. Choose the right subject for each sentence. Remember that subjects have a noun and may have an adjective. The noun will name a person, place or thing. Write the correct answers to the sentences.

a. ________________ were fun to play with at Tommy's house. (The big dogs, Running around)

b. ________________ helped us build the treehouse. (Walking, Daddy)

c. ________________flew up in the rose bush. (Faster, The red bird)

d. ________________ was in Aunt Mary's backyard. (A flower garden, Raining)

e. ________________were swaying in the wind. (Skating, Tree branches)

Chapter 4

Lesson 3: Regular & Irregular Plural Nouns

You can scan the QR code given below or use the url to access additional EdSearch resources including videos and mobile apps related to *Regular and Irregular Plural Nouns*.

Regular & Irregular Plural Nouns

URL	QR Code
http://www.lumoslearning.com/a/l21b	

Name: ______________________ Date: ____________

1. When there is more of one thing, some words need an "s" added to them. Examples: tree becomes trees, plane becomes planes. Singular means one and plural means more than one.

Some words must be changed to become plural.

If a noun ends in "lf", you change the "f" to a "v" and add "es".

Change the words from singular to plural.

wolf	
shelf	
leaf	
knife	
elf	

2. To make words ending in a "y" to plural, you change the "y" to "I" and add "es". Read the list of words below and make them plural.

butterfly	
fly	
story	
baby	

Name: ______________________ Date: ______________

3. **To make some words plural you add "es". Make the singular words match the plurals in the table below.**

potato	
tomato	
wish	
bench	
box	

4. **Sometimes when a noun becomes plural, the word changes all together. Read the sen tences below. The underlined word is singular and should be plural. Mark the correct plural noun.**

a.She was afraid of <u>mouse</u>.

Ⓐ mouses
Ⓑ mice

b.All the <u>person</u> were happy!

Ⓐ people
Ⓑ peoples

c.I heard so many <u>goose</u> honking at the park.

Ⓐ geeses
Ⓑ geese

d.Her <u>foot</u> had grown, and her shoes did not fit.

Ⓐ foots
Ⓑ feet

5. Match the plural nouns to the singular nouns.

men
women
children

child	
woman	
man	

6. Decide which way each singular noun was changed to a plural noun. Choose if an "s" was added, an "es", or a total new word. Mark the way the words were changed.

	Add "s"	Add "es"	Verb	Change word to new word
cat to cats				
dice to die				
dress to dresses				
tooth to teeth				
table to tables				

7. Remember the rule that you change the "f" in some nouns to "v" and add "es" to make them plural. Write your own sentence making the word below plural.

8. Some nouns do not change at all from singular (one) to plural (more than one). Read the sentences and mark the ones that have a noun that does not change.

Ⓐ The cows were eating in the field.
Ⓑ We saw many deer on the ranch.
Ⓒ The buffalo ran when the cars came by.
Ⓓ How many sheep do you see?

9. Underline the 3 plural words in the sentence below.

One day, the families took their children for a stroll in the woods.

10. Use the words below to complete the sentences with plural nouns. Some will not work. Remember the rules about plural nouns.

(child, classes, children, truck, trucks, class)

1. The ______________ love to play outside.

2. Students in all ______________ worked hard on the tests.

3. The big ______________ sped down the highway.

Chapter 4

Lesson 4: Reflexive pronouns

You can scan the QR code given below or use the url to access additional EdSearch resources including videos and mobile apps related to *Reflective pronouns*.

Reflective pronouns

URL	QR Code
http://www.lumoslearning.com/a/l21c	

Name: ______________________ Date: ______________

Reflexive pronouns tell about the subject. Example: herself, myself, ourselves, himself, themselves, yourself.

1. **Read the sentences and underline the reflexive pronoun in each sentence.**

The children helped themselves to cake.

I see myself as a ballerina.

Maggy knows how to sew by herself.

We tell ourselves to be nice to each other.

2. **Read the sentences and decide what is the subject and what is the reflexive pronoun in each one.**

1. I did it myself.

2. She made herself a cake.

3. We ran by ourselves to the park.

Subject	Reflexive pronoun

3. Choose the right reflexive pronoun for each sentence. Write it in the blank.

a. We understood the directions by ________________.
(themselves, ourselves)

b. She watched the baby by ________________.
(herself, himself)

c. They cannot do it ________________.
(ourselves, themselves)

d. He made the kite ________________.
(herself, himself)

4. Which of the following sentences does NOT have a reflexive pronoun in it?

Ⓐ Mark ran the mile by himself.
Ⓑ Sarah and Tammy played the piano.
Ⓒ Tyrone caught himself a huge fish.
Ⓓ They made pies themselves.

5. Complete the sentence with the right reflexive pronoun.

Did you learn that by ________?

Ⓐ himself
Ⓑ herself
Ⓒ yourself
Ⓓ ourselves

6. The sentence below is NOT in the right order for subject and reflexive pronoun. Read the sentence and rewrite it in the correct order. Be sure to use the correct capital and lower-case letter for the correct word order.

Themselves did it they.

Name: ______________________ Date: ______________

7. **Choose the right subject to go with the reflexive pronouns in each predicate to make the sentences complete.**

	We	You	I	He
am cooking it myself.				
fixed himself a sandwich.				
wanted to paint the doghouse ourselves.				
shouldn't go out by yourself in the dark.				

8. **Mark the sentences that use the reflexive pronouns correctly.**

Ⓐ Robert cut himself by accident.
Ⓑ She emailed yourself a picture of her cat.
Ⓒ Belinda read the book myself.
Ⓓ They made themselves soda floats.

9. **Another reflexive pronoun is itself. Itself is usually used to reflect something that is not a person, such as a kitten.**

Read the sentences below and Mark the 2 with "itself" used correctly as a reflexive pronoun.

Ⓐ The monkey likes to rub itself against the door.
Ⓑ The kitten often licks itself to get clean.
Ⓒ Itself was the best thing we found.
Ⓓ He was happy with itself.

10. **Write your own sentence using the reflexive pronoun that goes with I.**

Chapter 4

Lesson 5: Past tense of verbs

You can scan the QR code given below or use the url to access additional EdSearch resources including videos and mobile apps related to *Past tense of verbs*.

past tense of verbs

URL	QR Code
http://www.lumoslearning.com/a/l21d	

Name: ______________________________ Date: ______________

Verbs tell the action in a sentence. They are a part of the predicate. Some verbs can be changed from what is happening now (present tense) to what happened before (past tense). Most verbs are changed from present to past by adding an "ed". But some do not follow that rule. An irregular past tense verb is one where either the verb is changed to a new word or stays the same in present and past tense.

1. What do verbs do in a sentence? Mark the 2 best answers.

Ⓐ Verbs name the noun in the sentence.
Ⓑ Verbs tell the action in a sentence.
Ⓒ Verbs are words in a sentence that tell about the subject.
Ⓓ Verbs are part of the predicate.

2. Fill in the blank to answer the sentence about irregular verbs. Use what you read to help you.

An irregular past tense verb is one where either ______________________________

____.

3. Below is a list of present and past tense verbs. Mark the irregular verbs that tell what has already happened (past tense).

Ⓐ sat
Ⓑ hide
Ⓒ tell
Ⓓ ate
Ⓔ sit
Ⓕ hid
Ⓖ told
Ⓗ eat

Name: ______________________ Date: ____________

4. Read the sentences and pick the correct irregular past tense verb to answer each one.

a. Yesterday we ________ to the bus.
(run, ran)

b. Last Saturday, Mary _________ shopping with her mother.
(went, go)

c. They ________ the deer when they went on vacation a month ago.
(saw, see)

d. When I was in first grade, Mr. Samuel __________ me how to read.
(teach, taught)

5. Place each present tense verb in the column under its matching past tense verb.

Present tense	Past tense						
	knew	drew	found	took	drank	met	came
draw							
take							
know							
come							
meet							
find							
drink							

6. Read the story and underline the 5 past tense irregular verbs.

Sally and Tim went to the beach. They found seashells and starfish. Sally made them sandwiches. The kids ate the food. Then they swam in the ocean.

Name: ______________________ Date: ______________

7. **Find the sentence that does NOT have an irregular past tense verb in it.**

Ⓐ Aunt Valerie took the dog for a walk in the park.
Ⓑ She went to see the new building in town.
Ⓒ The baby held on tight to its bottle.
Ⓓ I hide from my big brother.

8. **The following is a list of present and past tense verbs. Underline the ones that have irregular past tense verbs.**

Ⓐ fly- flew
Ⓑ hear- heard
Ⓒ sleep-slept
Ⓓ play-played
Ⓔ walk-walked

9. **Remember that some verbs do not change from present to past tense. Underline the verbs in the sentences below that did not change spelling from present to past tense.**

He read the story many times.

They let Frank play with them yesterday.

When did you cut your hand?

He quit the team on Friday.

10. **Match the present tense verbs to their irregular past tense.**

stand	
drive	
grow	
fall	
choose	
freeze	

(froze, grew, stood, drove, fell, chose)

Chapter 4

Lesson 6: Simple and compound sentences

You can scan the QR code given below or use the url to access additional EdSearch resources including videos and mobile apps related to *Simple and compound sentences*.

Simple and compound sentences

URL	QR Code
http://www.lumoslearning.com/a/l21f	

Name: ______________________ Date: ______________

Sentences must have a subject (noun and any describing words) and predicate (verb and any helping words) to be complete. If words put together do not have both a subject and a verb they do not make a sentence. These words are phrases.

1. Let's look at the story below. Some of the words are not in a complete sentence. Underline the words (phrases) that are not a complete sentence.

Mary and Jane want. to go to the store. They got ready. Mary asked her mother. for some money. Her mother gave her $2. Jane got $5 from her dad.

1.1 Make the phrases that were not complete sentences, complete by putting them together. Be sure to take out the period and join the words. Write them below.

2. Write the 3 complete sentences from the story. Reread the story.

Mary and Jane want. to go to the store. They got ready. Mary asked her mother. for some money. Her mother gave her $2. Jane got $5 from her dad.

3. Read the phrases below. Fill the subject to the boxes to make the sentence complete.

Roberto and Miguel

The beautiful ponies

She

The chicken soup

Subject	Predicate
	were fun to ride.
	love to play football.
	was good to eat.
	brushed her hair.

4. Read the predicates and match them with the correct subjects. Use each one only one time to make the best sentences.

Betty
The racecar
The dish
The alarm

Predicate	Subject
sped down the hill.	
broke as it fell to the floor.	
started ringing when the fire began.	
rode her bike up the road.	

There can be simple complete sentences and compound complete sentences. Simple sentences contain one subject and one predicate. Compound sentences contain at least 2 subjects and 2 predicates and are joined by conjunctions such as and, or, but, nor, and because. When joining simple sentences, use a comma before the conjunction.

5. Read the story below and answer the questions. Underline the 4 compound sentences in the story.

Every Halloween, the family loved to make Jack-o-lanterns. Their mother bought the pumpkins, and everyone helped carve funny faces on them.

They decided they wanted to grow their own for next year.

Dad dug a garden for the family. He bought seeds to plant. Joshua and Kevin planted pumpkin seeds, and Mom watered the garden.

The boys watched the garden every day. Soon the seed began to sprout little plants. They tended the garden, so the plants grew bigger. Finally, the vines had blooms and little pumpkins started to form.

6. Read the sentences below and mark the compound ones.

Ⓐ We walked together to school yesterday.
Ⓑ Sammy wanted to learn archery, so he took lessons.
Ⓒ The monkeys climbed the trees and chimpanzees swung from branches.
Ⓓ Most kids like peanut butter and jelly sandwiches.

7. Choose one of the three conjunctions below and make a compound sentence. Be sure to join the 2 simple sentences together with the conjunction. Make sure the sentence is the best you can make with the conjunction you choose. Follow rules for capitals, and punctuation.

Conjunction: but, so, because

The pecan tree branches were blowing in the wind. The rose bushes stood still.

8. Choose the best conjunction for each compound sentence.

so

but

because

or

a. Teachers work hard, ________ the students can learn.

b. People ride to work on the bus, ___________ they do not want to drive.

c. I like to eat pizza, ___________Tommy likes hamburgers.

9. Which of the following is NOT a compound sentence? Mark your answer.

Ⓐ He helped his sister, so she could finish her project on time.
Ⓑ They wanted to ride their bikes, but it was raining.
Ⓒ They found the little skinny dog in their backyard.
Ⓓ Thomas and Freddy did their homework, but Sammy did not.

Chapter 4

Lesson 7: Understand Language conventions

You can scan the QR code given below or use the url to access additional EdSearch resources including videos and mobile apps related to *Understand Language conventions*.

Understand Language conventions

URL	QR Code
http://www.lumoslearning.com/a/l22	

Name: ______________________ Date: ______________

1. Underline the proper nouns in the sentences below.

The little puppy made Sarah very happy.
They went to see the show in Dallas Texas
If you love candy,you will love Valentine's Day!
John and Skipper played ball on Saturday.

2. The names of products are capitalized, too. An example is Cheetos. It names the snack. If you had the word chips, it would not be capitalized. It did not tell the product name of chips. Read the list in the box. Mark the ones that name or do not name a particular product.

	Names a particular product	Does not name a particular product
Cheerios cereal		
popcorn		
Skippy peanut butter		
Kraft cheese		

3. We know that a comma is used in a list of words, and to join clauses in sentences. Commas are also used in the headings and closings of letters. For example- Dear Mom, is an example of how to use a comma when you start a letter. For the closing of a letter here is an example- Yours truly, - then your name would go on the next line.

Read the list and Mark the ones that use a comma correctly.

Ⓐ Dear Mayor,
Ⓑ Thank, you
Ⓒ Dearest Grandma,
Ⓓ Respectfully,

4. **The apostrophe mark ' is used to combine two words into one word to make a contraction. If the word "not" is the second word in the sentence, take out the letter "o", put in the ' and make the contraction. Read the list of words and make them into contractions. Write the new word.**

a. should not = ____________

b. is not = ____________

c. did not = ____________

5. **Mark the words below that correctly show possession.**

Ⓐ Mike's
Ⓑ Daniels
Ⓒ Jess'
Ⓓ Cammies
Ⓔ Martha's

6. **When we read some words, we notice a spelling pattern. The spelling combination of "oi" and "oy" both make the same vowel sound as in boy. The patterns are used differently. Read the two rules below.**

1. If a word has a consonant then the pattern, and ends in a consonant, the spelling is "oi".

2. If a word has a consonant and the vowel pattern but no consonant at the end, the spelling is "oy".

Mark the words to show which spelling rule they follow.

	Rule #1	**Rule #2**
boil		
toy		
coy		
toil		

7. When a word has a short vowel sound at the end of the word where the "j" sound is heard, the spelling is "dge". If a word does not have a short vowel sound, the "j" sound is spelled "ge". Read the list of words in the box and mark the correct spelling for the "j" sound at the end of the words.

	dge	ge
age		
badge		
rage		
page		
fudge		
stage		
bridge		

8. There are many ways to help you understand new words. You can use a dictionary, thesaurus, a book or online encyclopedia. Read the definition of each reference material. Decide which one would be the best for the question given. Mark the best answer.

If I wanted to know how to use and sound out the word "hyperbole" which source would I use?

Ⓐ Dictionary- gives you the spelling, pronunciation, type of word (noun, verb, adjective, etc.) and how to use the word.
Ⓑ Thesaurus- gives you other words that are like the word.
Ⓒ Book- tells you about a topic or story.
Ⓓ Online encyclopedia- tells you about a topic.

Name: ______________________ Date: ______________

9. Guide words in a dictionary help you find the word. They are at the top of each page. The first guide word tells you what the first word on the page is, and the last one tells you the last word you will find on the page. Use what you already know about ABC order to search the page. An example would be

- Guide Words at top of page
- man monster
- Words that would be on this page:
- Mane
- Manger
- Mean
- Money

You could see that these words would be between man and monster in ABC order. Would the word Monday fall on this page? Write your answer and explain why or why not.

10. Capital letters are used at the beginning of proper (people, places, holidays) nouns. Some of the words below need to be capitalized to be correct. Fix those words and write them correctly on the line next to them. Leave the line blank if the word does not need to be capitalized.

stamps ___________

mary ___________

halloween ___________

tomorrow ___________

friday ___________

Chapter 4

Lesson 8: How is it Capitalized?

You can scan the QR code given below or use the url to access additional EdSearch resources including videos and mobile apps related to *How is it Capitalized?*

How is it Capitalized?

URL	QR Code
http://www.lumoslearning.com/a/l22a	

1. **Remember that holidays are always capitalized. Read the list of words and mark the holidays.**

   Ⓐ Easter
   Ⓑ Eggs
   Ⓒ Memorial Day
   Ⓓ Valentine's Day
   Ⓔ Presents

2. **Read the sentences below. Mark the one that uses capitalization correctly for holidays.**

   Ⓐ The family went on a vacation for the fourth of July.
   Ⓑ Mary and her mother made cupcakes for Veteran's Day.
   Ⓒ The team rode in a parade on president's day.
   Ⓓ Grandpa does not like halloween.

3. **Names of products are capitalized, too. Examples of these are Cheerios for a cereal, and Kraft for cheese or milk products. If an exact name is not there, do not capitalize it. Read the words in the box and mark if they should be capitalized.**

	Capitalize	**Do not capitalize**
Ford		
Truck		
Amazon		
Dog food		
M & M's		
Candy		
Store		
Coca Cola		

4. Read the sentences below. Mark the 2 that use product names correctly.

Ⓐ Most people like to eat Lay's chips.
Ⓑ He drove a bright shiny Toyota truck.
Ⓒ The dentist says to use crest toothpaste.
Ⓓ We feed our dog purina dog chow.

5. Fix the sentence below using the product names. Remember to capitalize the product name. Write it correctly.

His brother drove a chevrolet 4x4 truck, but his mom liked her buick car better.

6. Names of places must be capitalized, too. Countries, states, cities, landmarks, highways, and streets are examples of these. Read the words below. Make them capitalized.

a. main street ______________________

b. dallas, texas ______________________

c. japan ______________________

d. yellowstone national park ______________________

7. Read the sentences and underline the words that are names of places.

Rolando says Hawaii is the best place to go on a vacation.

Many people go to Washington Avenue to shop.

I have never visited England, but I want to go there one day.

My favorite store is Target.

8. Read the list of words below. Decide if they are names of places that need to be capitalized. Rewrite and capitalize the ones that are names of places. If there are 2 or more words, be sure to capitalize all of those that need to be.

big highway

tiny store

walmart

sears

disneyworld

chicago, illinois

9. Which of the following sentences does NOT have the correct use of capitalization of names of places.

Ⓐ Howard and Samantha took a trip to South America.
Ⓑ The best chicken nuggets are at McDonald's!
Ⓒ The train stopped in biloxi, mississippi.
Ⓓ We had fun at Six Flags!

10. Write the capitalized name of a place in a sentence.

San Francisco, California.

Chapter 4

Lesson 9: The Comma and Quotation Dilemma

You can scan the QR code given below or use the url to access additional EdSearch resources including videos and mobile apps related to *The Comma and Quotation Dilemma*

The Comma and Quotation Dilemma

URL	QR Code
http://www.lumoslearning.com/a/l22b	

1. Commas are used in greetings of letters and closings.

Choose the answers that are correct use of a comma in the greeting of a letter.

Ⓐ Dear Calvin,
Ⓑ Dearest Aunt Sue
Ⓒ Dearest Grandmother,
Ⓓ To Whom It May Concern,
Ⓔ Dear William

2. Read the letter. In both the start of a letter (salutation) and end of a letter (closing), a comma should be used at the end. Check and make the corrections if needed by adding a comma.

Dear Daddy

I would like to thank you for the gift of a new bike. It is the best gift ever. I love the basket on the front and the bright red color of the seat.

Thanks again

L' Toya

3. Mark the correct answer that shows how to use a comma at the beginning of the letter.

Ⓐ Dear David
Ⓑ Dear Tabitha
Ⓒ Dear Franklin
Ⓓ Dear Aunt Bea,

4. Read the following salutations. Fix the ones that are not correct by rewriting them with a comma.

To the President

Dear Eddie

Dear Mom,

Hello Friend,

5. Read the words in the box. Mark which would be a salutation (beginning of letter), and which would be a closing (end of letter).

	Salutation	Closing
Respectfully,		
Dear Greg,		
Thanks,		
Dearest Cousin Ida,		
Dear Jasmine,		

6. Read the letters below. Underline the letter that has correct use of the commas in both the salutation and closing.

1.Dear Katy,

We are inviting you to our house for the summer. It is by a lake and a park. We can go swimming and have picnics. Your parents have already said that you can come. I just wanted to send this letter to invite you myself!

Your friend forever

Belinda

2. Dear Katy,

We are inviting you to our house for the summer. It is by a lake and a park. We can go swimming and have picnics. Your parents have already said that you can come. I just wanted to send this letter to invite you myself!

Your friend forever,

Belinda

7. Make the closings correct by rewriting them.

Yours truly

Thanks

Best regards

Yours faithfully

Always

8. Read the salutations below. Read the letter. Choose the best one for the letter.

Ⓐ Dear Uncle Joseph,
Ⓑ Dearest Michael,
Ⓒ Dear Dad,
Ⓓ To the Landlord Mr. Jones,

Hi! I wanted to thank you for coming to visit us. You are my favorite uncle. I love the new doll you bought me. I showed it to all my friends. They said I must be your favorite niece! I laughed and said I was!

Love you bunches,

Veronica

9. If you were to write a letter to your closest friend, which closing would be the best? A letter to your friend would show a personal relationship. Mark your answer.

Ⓐ Respectfully,
Ⓑ Sincerely,
Ⓒ Thanks,
Ⓓ Yours always,

10. Which closing would be the best for a letter to a mayor? A letter to someone that is not a close friend should not close with a personal closing.

Ⓐ Best wishes,
Ⓑ Always,
Ⓒ Respectfully,
Ⓓ Yours always,

Chapter 4

Lesson 10: Use an apostrophe

You can scan the QR code given below or use the url to access additional EdSearch resources including videos and mobile apps related to *Use an apostrophe*

edSearch ***Use an apostrophe***

URL	QR Code
http://www.lumoslearning.com/a/l22c	

1. **Contractions are made by joining two words into one word and leaving out a letter. You put an ' in place of the missing letter to make the contraction. Some kinds of contractions combine a word with the word "are". The letter "a" is then left out and the 'put in. Some kinds combine a word with the word "is". The letter "i" is left out and the ' put in.Read the first word and second word in each row and write contractions in the contraction column**

First word	Second word	contraction
they	are	
we	are	
she	is	
he	is	
you	are	

2. **Which 2 sentences have contractions in them? Mark them.**

Ⓐ Jamie and I played in the park with our friends.
Ⓑ We aren't going to go shopping until Friday.
Ⓒ They're happy to go on vacation.
Ⓓ She ran home for supper.

3. **Write the contractions with the words below using not as the second word. Remember to leave out the "o" in not and add an '.**

a. are = ________

b. have = ________

c. did = ________

d. is = ________

4. **There are a couple of words that change completely when not is added as the second word and a contraction is made. Will not becomes won't and cannot becomes can't. Pick the sentence below that has one of these contractions in it. Mark your answer.**

Ⓐ Latifa can go into town with us.
Ⓑ The cows will eat their hay when it gets cold.
Ⓒ The firemen won't let the fire spread.
Ⓓ The police helped the lady cross the street.

5. **Read the sentences and choose the right contraction to put in each blank.**

a. They __________ sad anymore because they found their puppy. (aren't, can't)

b. The movie _______ going to start for one hour. (didn't, isn't)

c. _______ play video games after we do our homework. (Let's, You've)

d. She said _________ tried to make it before and failed. (I'm, she'd)

6. **When talking about something that belongs to someone, we call it possessive. If you are talking about a thing that belongs to someone, add an 's at the end of the person's or animal's name. If the word already ends in an "s" only add the '.**

Make the nouns possessive.

Nouns	Possessive
Manuel	
Tony	
Bess	
Emanuel	
Mr. Brown	
Ms. Bliss	

7. Which of the following groups of words do NOT show possession? Mark them.

Ⓐ Large dresses
Ⓑ Bonnie's friends
Ⓒ Natasha's pets
Ⓓ Fancy hats
Ⓔ Spicy cheeseburgers
Ⓕ Matilda's house

8. Read the sentences and mark 2 that use possessive nouns correctly.

Ⓐ Mr. Langleys class had a party today.
Ⓑ My sister's room is a mess!
Ⓒ He listens to Brad's music all the time.
Ⓓ Why did Todds dad get a job in another town?

9. Unscramble the words to make a sentence using the possessive noun correctly.

mother her keep let Patty's the tiny kitten.

10. Find the 4 possessives in the story and highlight them. One may be seen 2 times. Be sure to highlight all 4.

Mary's best friend was Vicky. Vicky's mom let them go to the park. The girls had fun. On the way home, they stopped at Vicky's favorite ice cream parlor. Beth and Susan were there, too. The girls' laughter was heard all over the store.

Name: _______________________ Date: _______________

Chapter 4

Lesson 11: Spelling patterns

You can scan the QR code given below or use the url to access additional EdSearch resources including videos and mobile apps related to *Spelling patterns*

Spelling patterns

URL	QR Code
http://www.lumoslearning.com/a/l22d	

1. Spelling has patterns in words that help us to remember how to spell them. Here is a pattern for spelling.

If a word has a short vowel sound and ends in the "k" sound, the "k" sound is spelled "ck".

Read the words below and Mark the ones that follow this rule.

Ⓐ Bike
Ⓑ Back
Ⓒ Rack
Ⓓ Stick
Ⓔ Flick
Ⓕ Brake
Ⓖ Like
Ⓗ Lake

2. If a word ends in the long "a" sound, the spelling pattern at the end is "ay".

Choose YES or NO for each word in the box to show if the word follows this rule.

	Yes	**No**
play		
stay		
away		
bake		
story		

3. A spelling pattern for long e words is that the long "e" is usually spelled with "ee" or "ea" and sometimes "ie" when followed by the letter "c". Long e can also be spelled e in short words such as me, he, she be, and we. The word "the" is not usually long "e", but the "e" says "u" like in duck.

Read the sentences below and Mark the long "e" spelled words. (Do not mark the word "the".) There can be more than one long "e" word in each sentence.

We looked for the cat that ran up the tree.
Sandra and I would like to eat a piece of chocolate cake.
Please wash your hands.
The ice will freeze in about an hour.

4. Read the words. Mark the ones that have the long "e" spelling.

Ⓐ Better
Ⓑ Beef
Ⓒ Step
Ⓓ Sleep
Ⓔ Meat
Ⓕ Met

5. Spelling patterns for long "o" are found when "oa" are together or when a cvcv (consonant, vowel, consonant, vowel) pattern is found where the first vowel is an "o".

Read the words below and write "long o" next to those who follow one of these patterns. Write short o next to the "short o" words.

a. Boat - ___________

b. Smoke - _____________

c. Stop - _________

d. logs - ___________

e. coat - ____________

f. float - ________

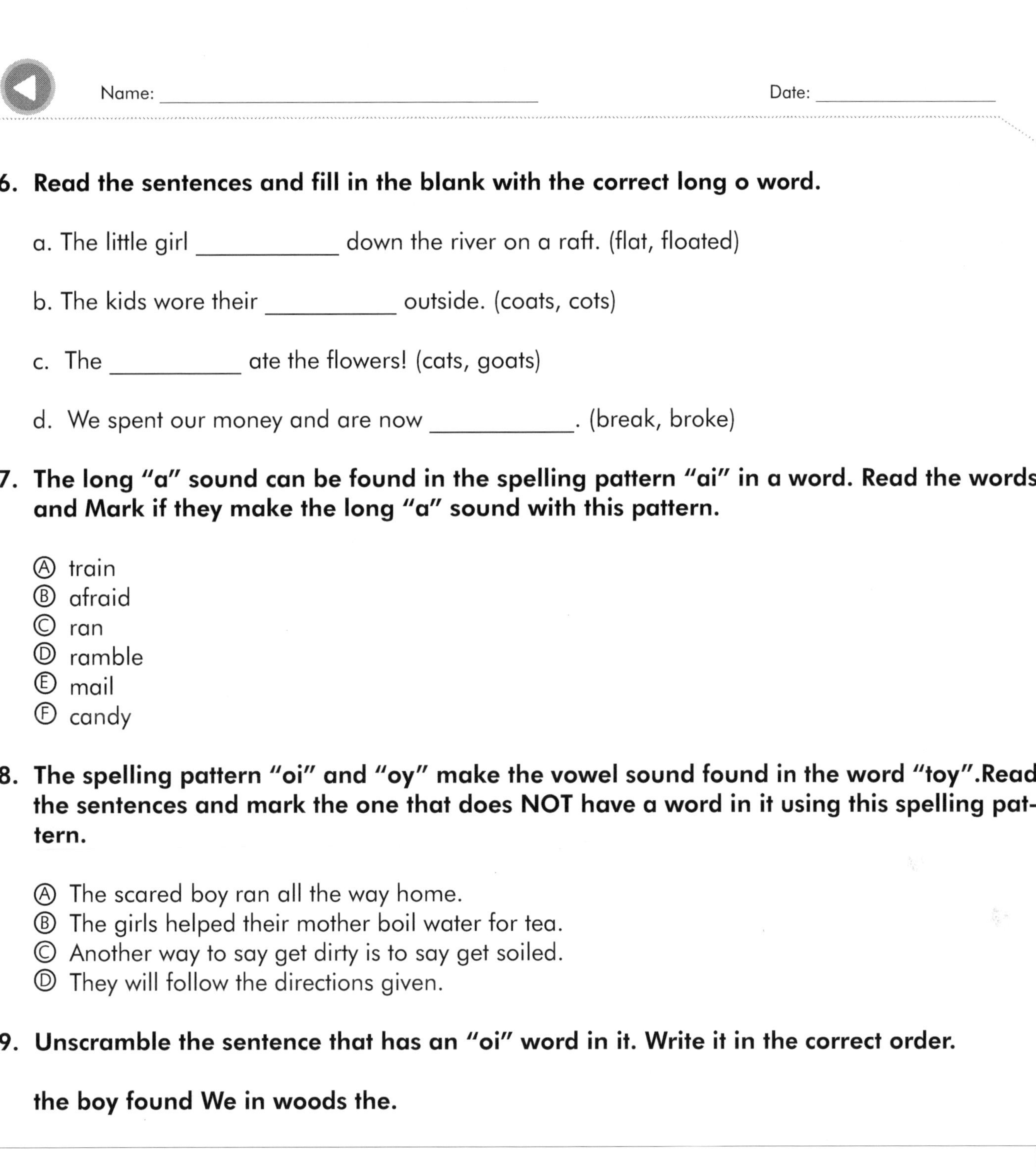

6. Read the sentences and fill in the blank with the correct long o word.

a. The little girl __________ down the river on a raft. (flat, floated)

b. The kids wore their __________ outside. (coats, cots)

c. The __________ ate the flowers! (cats, goats)

d. We spent our money and are now __________. (break, broke)

7. The long "a" sound can be found in the spelling pattern "ai" in a word. Read the words and Mark if they make the long "a" sound with this pattern.

Ⓐ train
Ⓑ afraid
Ⓒ ran
Ⓓ ramble
Ⓔ mail
Ⓕ candy

8. The spelling pattern "oi" and "oy" make the vowel sound found in the word "toy".Read the sentences and mark the one that does NOT have a word in it using this spelling pattern.

Ⓐ The scared boy ran all the way home.
Ⓑ The girls helped their mother boil water for tea.
Ⓒ Another way to say get dirty is to say get soiled.
Ⓓ They will follow the directions given.

9. Unscramble the sentence that has an "oi" word in it. Write it in the correct order.

the boy found We in woods the.

10. The long "e" sound can be in words that have 2 syllables. Read the words in the box and mark if they are or are not long "e" words that follow a 2-syllable pattern where the long "e" is in the first syllable.

	Follows long "e" pattern	**Does not follow pattern**
secret		
settle		
depend		
he		
even		

Chapter 4

Lesson 12: Consult reference materials

You can scan the QR code given below or use the url to access additional EdSearch resources including videos and mobile apps related to *Consult reference materials*

Consult reference materials

URL	QR Code
http://www.lumoslearning.com/a/l22e	

Name: ______________________ Date: ______________

1. **Dictionaries help you to spell, pronounce, and understand what words mean. The two guide words at the top of the pages show you if the word you want is on that page. The words on the page fall between the words in ABC order.**

   If I wanted to check the spelling of the word- giraffe- which guide words would I use in a dictionary? Mark the best answer.

   Ⓐ dairy - doghouse
   Ⓑ germ - great
   Ⓒ gem - get
   Ⓓ fairy - fun

2. **Read the sentence below. Then read the definitions for the words from a dictionary. Which word fits best in the sentence? Mark the answer.**

   He was ____________________ to see his friends.

   Ⓐ Explosive- might become violent, dangerous
   Ⓑ Excited- eager, enthusiastic, anticipating emotions
   Ⓒ Skinny- narrow, slender, thin

3. **Which 2 words need to be looked up in the dictionary to correct the spelling?**

   Ⓐ happy
   Ⓑ forgeting
   Ⓒ childran
   Ⓓ complete

4. **An online encyclopedia gives information about a topic. It can be used to help you write a report or understand more about something. Which 3 topics would you find the most information about in an online encyclopedia? Mark the ones that would help you research topics.**

   Ⓐ Funny
   Ⓑ Rainforest
   Ⓒ Trees
   Ⓓ Walking
   Ⓔ Cats

5. **The words below are not in ABC order to look up in a dictionary. Put them in the correct order.**

Ⓐ money
Ⓑ mistake
Ⓒ mean
Ⓓ multiply
Ⓔ missing

1	
2	
3	
4	
5	

6. **A thesaurus is another reference material. It is used to find words that are similar or opposite of a word you use. Sometimes you use a word too many times in a story and need to find a new word. Read the sentences and write the word that was used too many times.**

Brian likes to go fishing. He likes to walk to the lake. His dad likes to fish, too. They want to catch many fish.

7. Read the words and state whether the following synonyms are true or false.

Word	Synonyms	True or False
happy	cheerful, glad, joyful	
ran	raced, sped	
ate	fixed, corrected	

8. Antonyms mean the opposite. A thesaurus has antonyms for words. Which of the following groups of words are antonyms?

Ⓐ happy- sad
Ⓑ many- few
Ⓒ begin- start
Ⓓ on - off

9. Read the 2 lists of words. Mark the ones in the first list that had to be corrected after using a dictionary.

List 1

Ⓐ butiful
Ⓑ manage
Ⓒ impossible
Ⓓ frutful

List 2

1. beautiful
2. manage
3. impossible
4. fruitful

10. Read the definitions of reference materials and write the ones that would match what you need to do.

Dictionary- tells what a word means in ABC order, gives pronunciation, part of speech and a way to use the word.

Thesaurus- gives synonym (word that means the same), antonym (word that means the opposite), and part of speech in ABC order.

Atlas- maps of places around the world, geographical regions.

Encyclopedia- information on topics to help you understand and do research.

a. Look for where the state of Nevada is located. ________________

b. How to pronounce your spelling words. ________________

c. Find out more about elephants to write a paper for class. ________________

d. Words to use in a story that mean the same thing. ________________

Chapter 4

Lesson 13: Use knowledge of language and its conventions

You can scan the QR code given below or use the url to access additional EdSearch resources including videos and mobile apps related to *Use knowledge of language and its conventions*

Use knowledge of language and its conventions

URL	QR Code
http://www.lumoslearning.com/a/l23	

Read the story and answer the questions.

It was a nice sunny day outside. Noe and Kevin wanted to ride their bikes to the park. The boys were at Noe's house. They had ridden bikes the day before. Kevin had spent the night with Noe. When they got ready, they noticed their tires were low on air and they needed to fix them.

The boys looked in the garage. Luckily, they found a tire pump. In no time, they had their bikes ready to go!

1. Where were the boys? Mark the answer.

Ⓐ At the park
Ⓑ At Noe's grandma's house
Ⓒ At Kevin's house
Ⓓ At Noe's house

2. Who are the characters in the story? Write them.

3. What was the problem in the story? Write your own answer.

4. If you were to give a speech about making a sandwich which 2 sentences below would be the best ideas to use?

Ⓐ You could get the materials and make the sandwich while you were talking about it.
Ⓑ You could pass out notes to the class, so they could follow along.
Ⓒ You could eat the sandwich.
Ⓓ You could ask your little brother for help.

5. **When speaking to your class, what would you NOT want to do? Mark the best answer.**

Ⓐ Practice your speech
Ⓑ Keep good eye contact with the class
Ⓒ Speak slowly and ask for questions at the end of your speech
Ⓓ Look down at the floor while speaking

Read the story and answer the question.

Most kids like to have pets. A pet can keep you company during the day. Some pets can be taught to do tricks. Dogs like to fetch balls or sticks. They can also learn to follow commands like sit, lay down, and roll over. Cats are not very good at tricks but can play with string or yarn. Pets can be very loving. Pets need food.

6. **What sentences follow the story?**

Ⓐ Pets can keep you company.
Ⓑ Pets can learn tricks.
Ⓒ Pets need food.
Ⓓ Kids like to have pets.

7. **The last sentence in the story does NOT follow the story. Pets need food. Why does it NOT follow the story?Mark your answer.**

Ⓐ The story talks about pet food.
Ⓑ The story does not talk about feeding your pet.
Ⓒ The story tells everything about having a pet.
Ⓓ The story tells about what dogs and cats like to eat.

8. **Think of a better ending sentence and write it.**

9. When you listen to someone talking or speaking, you need to pay attention to what they say.

Pick 2 sentences that show ways to be a good listener.

Ⓐ Keep your eyes on the speaker.
Ⓑ Draw pictures.
Ⓒ Take notes to help you remember what they said.
Ⓓ Close your eyes and think of something else.

10. Mark the sentences in the box to show what to or not to do while listening to someone

Word	Good Listening	Not good listening
Pay attention to the speaker.		
Read a book		
Show interest or ask questions afterward		

Name: ______________________ Date: ______________

Chapter 4

Lesson 14: Formal and Informal language

You can scan the QR code given below or use the url to access additional EdSearch resources including videos and mobile apps related to *Formal and Informal language*

Formal and Informal language

URL	QR Code
http://www.lumoslearning.com/a/l23a	

We speak in different ways when we talk to different people.

Informal speaking is a way we talk to friends and relatives. Formal speaking is a way we talk to people we do not know very well.

1. Read the names in the box and mark if we would talk to them informal or formal.

Word	Informal	Formal
Mother		
Classmate		
Best friend		
Mayor		
President		
Grandma		

2. Read the sentences and write formal or informal after each one.

a. "Hey, let's go swimming!"

b. "Your Honor, would like to invite you to attend our banquet."

c. "This is to inform you of your required attendance."

d. "Let's get this party going!"

e. "Mr. President, we are proud of you."

3. Which 2 sentences are informal?

Ⓐ "Mom, I am hungry!"
Ⓑ "Enter the building through the door."
Ⓒ "Pay your bill on time."
Ⓓ "Yeah, we won the game!"

4. Your teacher told the class to write a letter to the City Council. Which type of English would you use? Formal or Informal?

4.1. Why would you write it in this way? Explain.

5. Read the sentence below. It is informal.

Then choose the sentence that would be formal. Mark the best answer.

"We had a blast at the zoo!"

Ⓐ What a fantastic time we had at the zoo, guys!
Ⓑ We had a good time visiting the zoo today.
Ⓒ Super time at the zoo today! yelled Mark.

6. Read the paragraph. Find the sentence that shows informal use of English. Write the sentence.

The class went on a field trip to visit the Corpus Christi Art Museum. Everyone was having a great time. Suddenly, Sara shouted, "Wow! Check out this painting of a zebra!" The students all turned to look.

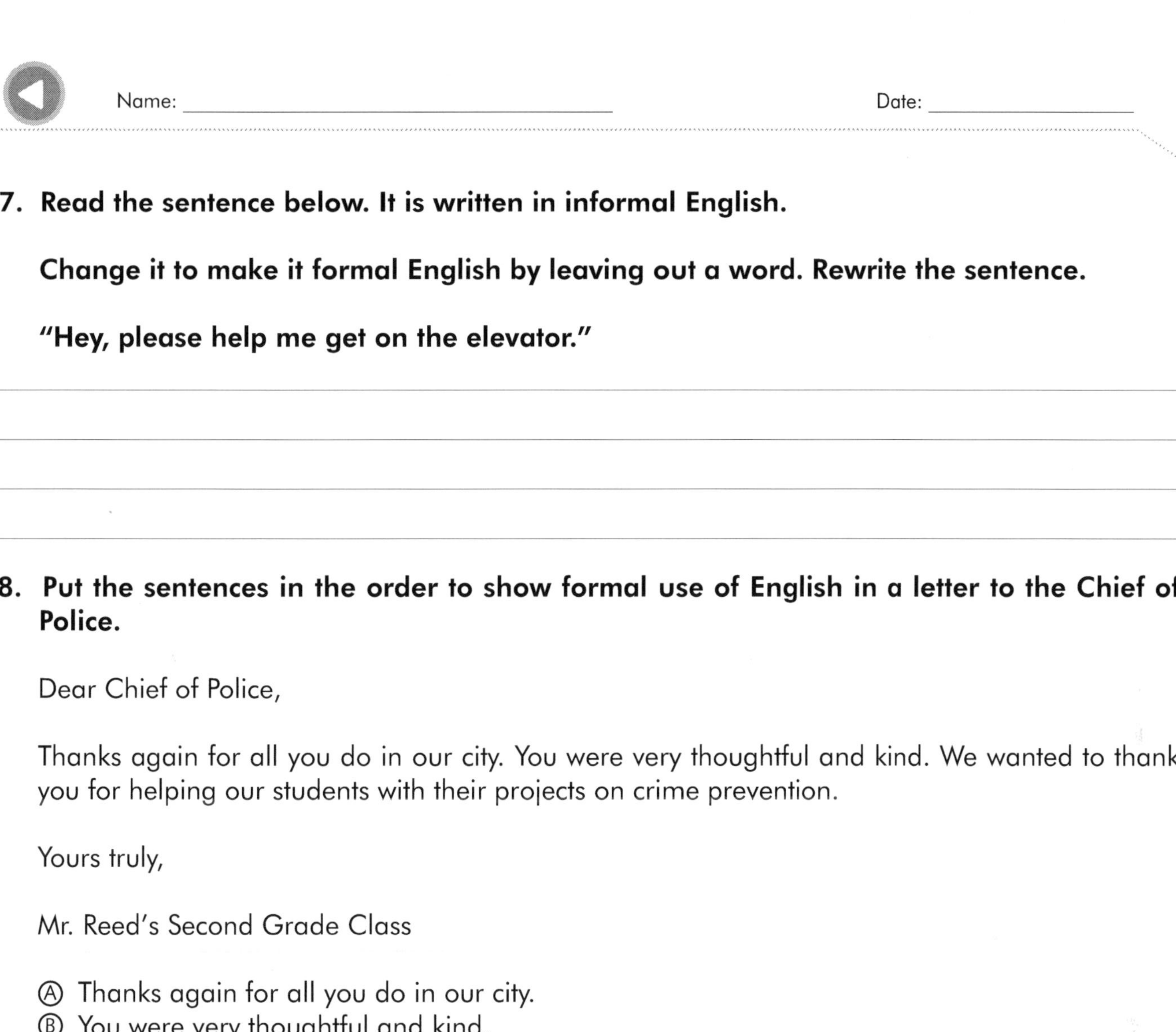

7. **Read the sentence below. It is written in informal English.**

Change it to make it formal English by leaving out a word. Rewrite the sentence.

"Hey, please help me get on the elevator."

8. **Put the sentences in the order to show formal use of English in a letter to the Chief of Police.**

Dear Chief of Police,

Thanks again for all you do in our city. You were very thoughtful and kind. We wanted to thank you for helping our students with their projects on crime prevention.

Yours truly,

Mr. Reed's Second Grade Class

Ⓐ Thanks again for all you do in our city.
Ⓑ You were very thoughtful and kind.
Ⓒ We wanted to thank you for helping our students with their projects on crime prevention.

9. Put the sentences in the best order to show informal use of English in a letter to Uncle Bobby.

Dearest Uncle Bobby,

I had always wanted my own pair of skates! Hey, Unc! Looking forward to seeing you next week! Thanks for the super surprise that I got in the mail.

Love always,

Sammy

Ⓐ I had always wanted my own pair of skates!
Ⓑ Hey, Unc! Looking forward to seeing you next week!
Ⓒ Thanks for the super surprise that I got in the mail.

10. Write your own sentence in informal English to tell your friend, Jerome, about your trip to the beach.

Chapter 4

Lesson 15: Same Word Different Meanings

You can scan the QR code given below or use the url to access additional EdSearch resources including videos and mobile apps related to *Same Word Different Meanings*

Same Word Different Meanings

URL	QR Code
http://www.lumoslearning.com/a/l24	

Name: ______________________ Date: ____________

Homographs are words that are spelled the same, can sound the same, but have different meanings.

1. Read the story and answer the questions.

Eddie and his friends were on a baseball team. He loved to play <u>second</u> baseman on his team. When the other team was up to <u>bat</u>, he was ready by his base. He could catch a <u>fly</u> ball easily.

One day, he hurt his <u>ear</u> when the ball clipped by it. Eddie heard the ball whizzing by him. It stung him, but he was able to catch it with his right <u>hand</u>. The player was out!

What is the meaning of the word second in the story?

Ⓐ A short amount of time
Ⓑ What comes after first

2. What is the meaning of the word bat in the story?

Ⓐ Baseball equipment
Ⓑ A mammal that has wings and flies

3. Which sentence helps you imagine the sound of the ball going by? Mark the best answer.

Ⓐ He could catch a fly ball easily.
Ⓑ Eddie heard the ball whizzing by him.
Ⓒ The player was out!

4. Match the definitions to the underlined words in the story.

	Part of a corn plant	a ball caught after being hit in a baseball game.	a body part used to hear with	a group of cards in a card game	an insect	a body part with fin-gers and a thumb on it
fly						
hand						
ear						

5. **Read the sentence below and choose the answer that explains the underlined phrase in the sentence. A simile is when something is compared to something else using the words "like" or "as".**

   She ate so much she felt <u>like an over -inflated balloon.</u>

   Ⓐ A simile that compares her looks to a balloon.
   Ⓑ A simile that compares her eating to that of a balloon with too much air in it.

A metaphor is a direct comparison. An example is-Life is a bowl of cherries. A bowl of cherries is the comparison to life completing the metaphor. Metaphors do not use like, or as.

6. **Read the sentences below and Mark those sentences that contain a metaphor.**

   Ⓐ Mrs. Jones' classroom was a zoo.
   Ⓑ My room is like a jungle.
   Ⓒ Time is money.
   Ⓓ The van was a heater in the summer afternoon.

Read the story and answer the questions. There may be new words that you do not know. Try to sound them out or read around the words to help you determine their meaning in the story.

Every year the entire school waits for "Play Day". It happens after the state tests and before the last week of school. They <u>schedule</u> it to be held starting at 10:00am and runs until half an hour before school is <u>dismissed</u>. The students have a hot dog and hamburger lunch cooked by the principal. They have a break after lunch, so they do not get <u>heat exhaustion</u>. Each grade level <u>participates</u> in events for their physical ability level. They all play the games and do the activities. Winners in the games and activities get prizes and ribbons. All the students receive a participation certificate.

7. **What does the underlined word <u>schedule</u> mean in the story? Choose the best answer.**

   Ⓐ to cancel
   Ⓑ to plan
   Ⓒ to decide
   Ⓓ to ignore

8. What does the underlined word <u>dismissed</u> mean in the story? Choose the best answer.

Ⓐ started fresh
Ⓑ left behind
Ⓒ stopped or released
Ⓓ paused for a time

9. Which of the following sentences explains why the students have a break after lunch? Mark the answer.

Ⓐ The students have a hot dog and hamburger lunch cooked by the principal.
Ⓑ Due to the heat of the day, students have a break after lunch, so they do not get heat exhaustion.

10. Which of the following sentences explains which students participate in "Play Day"? Mark your answer.

Ⓐ They all play the games and do the activities.
Ⓑ Winners in the games and activities get prizes and ribbons.

Chapter 4

Lesson 16: Prefix and Suffix

You can scan the QR code given below or use the url to access additional EdSearch resources including videos and mobile apps related to *Prefix and Suffix*

URL	QR Code
http://www.lumoslearning.com/a/l24b	

Prefixes are letters added to words to form new words with different meanings. Read the prefix and what it means.

1. **Write the definitions of each new word that is made when the prefix is added.**
   For example- unlocked- not locked.
   un - not

   a. unhappy- ______________

   b. unopened- __________

   c. unable- ___________

   d. unknown- ____________

2. **Read the sentences below. Mark the sentence that has a prefix word in it that means "not".**

   Ⓐ He isn't going to the fair because he is sick.
   Ⓑ She untied her shoelaces.
   Ⓒ He is looking for the answer to the question.
   Ⓓ She will reread the book to better understand it.

3. **Read the prefix and what it means.**

   Write the definitions of each new word that is made when the prefix is added.
   Example: remake – make again re – again, back

   a. reread- _________________

   b. replay - ___________________

   c. redo - ________________

4. **The prefix "pre" means before. Read the sentences and underline the words that have this prefix in it.**

   Her little sister went to preschool in the city.

   Mom had to preheat the oven before she could cook her supper.

5. **The words "bicycle" and "tricycle" have prefixes. Think of how many wheels are in each. This will help you with your answers.**

What do these prefixes mean? Write your answer in words, not numbers.

prefixes	numbers
bi	
tri	

6. **Which sentence does NOT have a prefix word in it?**

Ⓐ Mr. Adams told the class to reread the assignment.
Ⓑ We looked and looked but did not see the return item.
Ⓒ She was very happy and excited to see her aunt.
Ⓓ He rode his bicycle to the store.

7. **Read the scrambled words that have prefixes in them. Remember a prefix comes at the beginning of a word and changing the meaning of the word.**

scrambled words	word
happyun	
schoolpre	
readre	
likedis	

8. **Find the 2 sentences that contain prefixes. Mark your answers.**

Ⓐ He didn't preview the music he played.
Ⓑ The park was open late, so the fair could go on.
Ⓒ Every time we go to town, our dog wants to go to!
Ⓓ It is unlikely that I passed that test.

9. Read the words in the box below. If they have a prefix in them mark Yes, if not No.

	Yes	No
preview		
ringing		
lived		
unkind		

10. Read the sentences and choose the right meaning of the underlined word.

1. Sushi is <u>uncooked</u> fish.

Ⓐ very cooked
Ⓑ not cooked
Ⓒ grilled
Ⓓ well done

2. Aunt Gladys saw a <u>preview</u> of the new show.

Ⓐ watched later
Ⓑ watched again
Ⓒ watched before others
Ⓓ watched after

3.The singer had to <u>repeat</u> the song.

Ⓐ undo
Ⓑ before
Ⓒ never
Ⓓ do again

Name: ____________________ Date: ____________

Chapter 4

Lesson 17: Adjectives and adverbs

You can scan the QR code given below or use the url to access additional EdSearch resources including videos and mobile apps related to *Adjectives and adverbs*

Adjectives and adverbs

URL	QR Code
http://www.lumoslearning.com/a/l21e	

Name: ______________________ Date: ______________ 

Adjectives and adverbs are words used in sentences. Adjectives tell about nouns while adverbs tell about verbs, adjectives or another adverb.

1. Read the list of noun phrases. Write the adjectives.

noun phrases	adjectives
purple flowers	
second-grade teacher	
yellow bright light	
funny smile	
grumpy old man	
good grades	

2. Read the sentences and mark the one with 3 adjectives in it.

Ⓐ The pretty little lady was looking for her tiny kitten.
Ⓑ She lost her book and was very sad.
Ⓒ Don't play in the rain today.
Ⓓ We like our cupcakes very much.

3. Choose the correct adjective that will make the sentence correct. Mark your answer.

The _____ pillow helped me sleep.

Ⓐ loudly
Ⓑ first-grade
Ⓒ fluffy
Ⓓ well

Name: ______________________ Date: ______________

4. Choose the correct adjective for each sentence.

Sentence	Adjectives	correct adjective
We are _____ spellers.	well, good	
The _____ spider scared us.	always, huge	
The _______ bike was fun to ride.	very, orange	
My ______ sister let me go with her.	sweet, sweetly	

5. Match the adjectives with their nouns in the box. Pick the best answers and use them only one time.

	diamond	parrot	chest	cactus
giant squawking				
white shiny				
green prickly				
brown wooden				

6. Choose the sentence with the adverb in it.

Ⓐ He walked to the street.
Ⓑ She quietly went to her room to study.
Ⓒ They listen to their teacher.
Ⓓ We will not go outside today because of the weather.

7. Mark the adverbs in the list below. Remember that an adverb tells about a verb, another adverb or about an adjective.

Ⓐ pretty
Ⓑ slowly
Ⓒ beautiful
Ⓓ tiny
Ⓔ very
Ⓕ well
Ⓖ gladly

8. Underline the adverbs in the sentences below.

He did his work well.

She walked proudly across the stage.

He took his time to do the test carefully.

The car slowly came to a stop.

9. Read the list of words in the box below. Mark if the words are adjectives or adverbs.

	Adjectives	**Adverb**
correctly		
silently		
breakable		
golden		

10. Two words-good and well-are often used the wrong way. Good is an adjective and well is an adverb. Read the sentences below and choose good or well in the blanks.

a. The students did very _________ on their science project.

b. They had _________ science projects.

Chapter 4

Lesson 18: The Context Clue

You can scan the QR code given below or use the url to access additional EdSearch resources including videos and mobile apps related to *The Context Clue*.

URL	QR Code
http://www.lumoslearning.com/a/l24a	

Name: ______________________ Date: ______________

Context clues can be words or phrases in sentences that help you to understand what the meaning of the sentence is when you are reading.

Context clues are usefull in undestanding words that are spelled the same, sound the same, but have different meanings.

1. Read the sentences below. Underline the words that are spelled and sound the same but have different meanings In each pair of sentences.

He broke his big toe.
She spent her money and was broke now.
The iron nail was rusty.
Mom will iron Dad's shirt.
The cave was dark.
The rain made the roof cave in.

2. Read the words and sentences. Choose the word that will make sense. Be careful as some words sound the same but are spelled differently and mean different things. Other words are spelled the same but have different meanings when used. Write the words in the blanks that belong. A word can be used more than one time.

mind
flower
flour
handle
stare

1. The handle of the milk jug was slippery.	
2. I always mind my parents.	
3. She did not stare at the strange looking car.	
4. What kind of flower is your favorite?	
5. What's on your mind?	
6. You need to use flour when you make a cake.	

3. Some words are rhyming words. Read the words and match them to their rhyming words in the box.

sing ______________

fox ______________

believe ______________

scout ______________

Ⓐ about
Ⓑ relieve
Ⓒ ring
Ⓓ box

4. Read the words below. Underline the two words in each row that sound the same but mean something different.

pies piece peace

knows nose knew

4.1 Using context clues, choose the right words from number 4 above to fill in the blanks in the sentences below.

1. He wants a ____ of cake.	
2. When the baby sleeps, we have ______ and quiet.	
3. She has a pretty little ______.	
4. Callie _____ all her multiplication facts.	

5. Read the words below. Highlight the two words in each row that sound the same but mean something different.

stick stake steak

weight wait white

5.1 Using context clues, choose the right words from number 5 above to fill in the blanks in the sentences below.

1. Mr. Brown put a _____ in the ground to mark the garden.	
2. Dad cooks _____ on the outdoor grill.	
3. Mom said to _____ to go swimming.	
4. The _____ of the trunk was over 100 pounds.	

6. Choose the sentence that is correct. Mark your answer.

Ⓐ The garden is mind to water.
Ⓑ He doesn't mind helping his sister with her homework.
Ⓒ She and her friend think that the flour is pretty.
Ⓓ He likes to star at the clouds in the sky.

7. Read the definitions of the words. Then choose the word that best fits each sentence.

Hare- a rabbit

Hair- what grows on our head

a. The _____ of the fair princess was golden.

b. The _____ ran when the dogs chased him.

8. If you wanted to write a story using a word that tells about things being calm, quiet, and happy, what word would you use? Mark the word.

Ⓐ piece
Ⓑ peace

9. Read the sentences. Choose the best definition of the underlined word. The words in both sentences will help you decide.

1. We couldn't believe how far the ball went. Nathan <u>hurled</u> it across the field.	threw hard dropped	
2. Aunt Reba was shocked by the <u>curt</u> owner's voice. She was not expecting to be treated badly.	rude honest	

10. Antonyms and synonyms help people to understand the sentence thought. Antonyms mean the opposite and synonyms mean the same. Read the words and choose the synonyms.

Ⓐ easy, hard
Ⓑ huge, gigantic
Ⓒ cold, freezing
Ⓓ noisy, quiet
Ⓔ begin, start

Name: ______________________ Date: ______________

Chapter 4

Lesson 19: Roots and Affixes

You can scan the QR code given below or use the url to access additional EdSearch resources including videos and mobile apps related to *Roots and Affixes*.

URL	QR Code
http://www.lumoslearning.com/a/l24c	

Root words are main words. If letters are added to a root word, it becomes a new word. An example: help + ful = helpful.

1. Read the sentences and decide which is the best definition of the underlined word.

The students need additional time to finish their work.

Ⓐ less
Ⓑ excellent
Ⓒ larger
Ⓓ more

1.1 We were thankful that our cat was not hurt.

Ⓐ full of thanks
Ⓑ not happy
Ⓒ full of regret
Ⓓ very sad

1.2 It was thoughtful of her to help the elderly lady.

Ⓐ rude
Ⓑ kind
Ⓒ useless
Ⓓ not important

2. Make new words by adding the ending to the root word. Write your answers.

care + ful =	
hope + less =	
break + able =	
thank + ful =	

3. Read the words and decide which endings were added to make the new words. Write the ending next to each word.

comfortable = ________

hopeless = ________

respectful = ________

playful = ________

4. Read the words in the box and write the correct root word for each of them.

Word	Word	Word	Root word
respectful	respected	respects	
careless	careful	caring	
playful	played	playing	
breakable	breaking	breaks	

5. Read the word and definition. Write your answers in each sentence.

careful – taking care

comfortable – relaxed

appearance- the look of someone or something

playful – liking to play

a. Margaret felt ____________ during the contest. (careful, comfortable, appearance, playful)

b. His ______________ was a thrill to the crowd. (careful, comfortable, appearance, playful)

c. The kitten was ______________. (careful, comfortable, appearance, playful)

d. We were ______________ not to make any noise when the baby was sleeping. (careful, comfortable, appearance, playful)

6. Use the root word kind, add <u>ness</u> to it. Make a sentence with the new word.

7. Unscramble the words to make a correct sentence using the root word with its ending. Write the sentence. Hint: Begin the sentence with the word- It.

careless was it him to drop of trophy the.

8. Read the sentences. Write the root word for each underlined word. Remember the root word is the main word without an ending added to it.

1. David and Maria were <u>respectful</u> of their grandmother.	
2. She was <u>careful</u> as she handled the vase.	
3. We were <u>thankful</u> to get a new car.	
4. The team was <u>mindful</u> of the rules of the game.	

9. Add an ending to the root word to make the sentence correct. Mark your answer to fill in the blank.

The children were care______ and broke the window.

Ⓐ ful
Ⓑ able
Ⓒ less
Ⓓ ness

10. The words below are not written correctly. Rewrite them correctly.

HINT: The root word in these words comes first.

fulart	
nesskind	
fulcare	
anceappear	

Chapter 4

Lesson 20: Connecting related words

You can scan the QR code given below or use the url to access additional EdSearch resources including videos and mobile apps related to *Connecting related words*.

Connecting related words

URL	QR Code
http://www.lumoslearning.com/a/l24d	

Name: ______________________ Date: ______________

Compound words are made by joining two words to make a new word.

1. Read the words and write the compound words next to them.

ham + burger =	
pop + corn =	
milk + shake =	
butter + fly =	
tooth + brush =	

2. Read the list of words and make new compound words from other words in the list. Write them in ABC order.

ball
bell
home
end
foot
work
week
door

3. Read the sentences and underline the compound word in each sentence.

1. Chloe loves to go horseback riding.
2. Sam got a new skateboard!
3. What is wrong with Grandma?
4. Someone found my lost dog.
5. Watermelon is my favorite dessert.

4. Which compound word would be used if I am talking about something I carry my books in? Mark your answer.

Ⓐ firewood
Ⓑ snowman
Ⓒ backpack
Ⓓ cupcake

5. Read the words in the box. Mark if they ARE or ARE NOT compound words.

	Compound word	Not a compound word
walking		
sidewalk		
pancake		
because		

6. Read the compound words below and put them in the correct sentences. Use the words only one time. Be sure to read each sentence carefully.

(snowman, highway, cheeseburger, birdhouse)

a. Mark and his dad built a ________________ to hang in the tree.

b. Every year we make a ________________ when it snows.

c. Grandpa had to drive a long way down the ________________.

d. Her favorite food to eat is a ________________.

7. The two compound words below are opposites. Read the sentences and decide which one belongs in each sentence. Write your answers.

inside
outside

a. We play football ______________.

b. Mother dusts the shelves ______________ the house.

8. In the sentences below, two words need to be combined to make a compound word. Underline the 2 words in each sentence that should be a compound word.

1. He wanted to play base ball when he was just 4 years old.

2. Bonnie does not like to ride the skate board.

3. Straw berries are delicious!

4. Be careful when you clean the fish bowl!

8.1 Write the new compound words that should be made in sentences from the question number 8 above.

9. Use the compound word below in a sentence. Write your sentence.

cupcake

10. Read the words below. They are not compound words because the order of the words is not correct. Write them in the correct compound word.

not compound words	correct compound word
flowersun	
lightmoon	
yardback	
boatsail	
thingsome	

Chapter 4

Lesson 21: Find the meaning

You can scan the QR code given below or use the url to access additional EdSearch resources including videos and mobile apps related to *Find the meaning*.

URL	QR Code
http://www.lumoslearning.com/a/l24e	

Name: ______________________ Date: ______________

1. **Read the definitions of the word below. Choose which definition you would use to answer the question.**

   a. cooler- adj., to get colder

   b. cooler- noun, a container used to keep food cold.

   Which definition would match the sentence below? 1a or 1b?

   John put the cokes in the cooler.

2. **Read the definitions of the words below. Write the word that would make sense in the sentence.**

   troop- noun, a group of soldiers

   toupee-noun, (too-pay) a small wig used to cover a bald spot

   The old man wore a funny ____________ on his head.

3. **Guide words tell which words can be found on a page in a dictionary. The words are listed on each page in ABC order beginning with the first guide word and ending with the second guide word. Look at the dictionary guide words below. Mark the words that would be on that page.**

   nose nutty

   Ⓐ now
   Ⓑ open
   Ⓒ never
   Ⓓ nut
   Ⓔ novel
   Ⓕ problem
   Ⓖ nuance

4. **Choose the words that would NOT fall on a page with the guide words below. Mark them.**

---

elephant even

Ⓐ eleven
Ⓑ elk
Ⓒ ending
Ⓓ deliver
Ⓔ every
Ⓕ empty
Ⓖ everything

5. **Read the definitions and the question. Some definitions are nouns (name something) or adjectives (tell about or describe something). Choose the best answer.**

Which word would help you describe a color of a car?

Ⓐ emerald- noun, a green gem
Ⓑ topaz- noun, a yellow mineral used in jewellery
Ⓒ sapphire- noun, a bright blue gem
Ⓓ turquoise- noun, bluish green material used in jewelry
Ⓔ amber- adj., dark orange or yellow color

Name: ______________________ Date: ______________

A glossary can be found at the end of some books. A glossary can be at the end of chapters of a textbook, too. The glossary tells you the definition of new words or important words. Read the glossary below. Answer the questions.

emu- a large Australian bird that does not fly, runs fast and looks like an ostrich

expedite- make an action happen quickly

futuristic- having or involving modern technology

geographical- based on physical features

justify- show or prove to be right

landmark- an object or place that is easy to recognize or see

monopolized- obtained control of by one person or group

6. Use two of the glossary words to complete the sentence.

The well- known ______________ helped the scientist find the __________________ location.

7. Use two of the glossary words to complete the sentence.

He ___________the meeting to________ his opinion.

Ⓐ emu
Ⓑ expedite
Ⓒ futuristic
Ⓓ geographical
Ⓔ justify
Ⓕ landmark
Ⓖ monopolized

8. Which of the words in the glossary means a type of bird? Write your answer.

Name: ______________________ Date: ______________

9. **Dictionaries can be in print, book or online. Below are the links and names of some online dictionaries. Which one would you look up if you were looking for an easy to use student dictionary? Mark your answer.**

Ⓐ Dictionary of Biology- Oxford Reference,www.oxfordreference.com
Ⓑ American Heritage Dictionary,https://www.ahdictionary
Ⓒ Britannica Kidshttps://kids.britannica.com

10. **The following definitions are found in a dictionary for the word "match". Read the definitions. Write the definition number next to the right sentences in the box.**

Match-

1. (noun) contest where people compete against each other in sports.

2. (noun) person or thing that resembles another

3. (noun) piece of wood used to start a fire with a tip that ignites.

	noun, contest where people compete against each other in sports.	noun, person or thing that resembles another	noun, piece of wood used to start a fire with a tip that ignites.
He struck the match to light the campfire wood.			
They were a perfect match.			
I played in the tennis match.			

Chapter 4

Lesson 22: The meaning of words

You can scan the QR code given below or use the url to access additional EdSearch resources including videos and mobile apps related to *The meaning of words*

URL	QR Code
http://www.lumoslearning.com/a/l25	

Name: ______________________ Date: ____________

Words can be related to each other in their meaning. Some words can be weaker or stronger than others. Example: big, gigantic would be in order from weaker to stronger.

1. Read the words below. Put them in the box in order from weaker to stronger meaning.

frightened

afraid

Weaker	Stronger

2. Choose the words that describe more than the underlined words in the sentences. Write them in the blanks.

frightened
awful
gorgeous
gigantic

a. Their dresses were very pretty.

b. Madeline was very scared when she saw the lion.

c. The spoiled milk tasted very bad.

d. The elephant was very big.

3. **Read the words and sentences below. Write the correct antonym for the underlined words.**

(closed, yes, play, there)

1. She said no to her mother.	
2. They wanted to work.	
3. The door was open.	
4. We were here when it started to rain.	

4. **Some words that help us to read and write are opposites of other words. They are called antonyms.**
Read the words below and match them to their antonyms.

short	
happy	
left	
fast	
on	
hot	

(cold, sad, tall, slow, right, off)

Name: ______________________ Date: ______________

5. Sometimes, when we use an adverb in a sentence, we must change the ending. Example: That dog was skinny. The other dog was skinnier. He was the skinniest dog we had ever seen.

The word skinny needs to be changed to skinnier and skinniest to make sense in the sentences.

Read the words below. Change the endings by adding "er" and then "est" to make new words. If the word ends in a "y" change the "y" to an "i" before adding the ending.

Word	adding "er"	adding "est"
happy		
thin		
big		
angry		

6. Read the sentences below and choose a word that would mean the same as the underlined word. (synonym) Highlight the words.

1. The <u>trash</u> smelled horrible. (garbage, garden)

2. She was <u>happy</u> about the award. (angry, joyous)

3. It was a <u>smart</u> move.(upsetting, brilliant)

4. He <u>looked</u> at the homework assignment. (stared, stopped)

7. Which sentence below uses a synonym for the word sweet? Mark the sentence.

Ⓐ He was excited to see his sister win the prize.
Ⓑ The icing on the cake was sugary tasting.
Ⓒ Brad scooted to the store on his bike.
Ⓓ Where did the sour grapes come from?

8. Read the words in the box, mark if they are antonyms or synonyms of each other.

	Antonyms	**Synonyms**
sweet, sour		
clean, dirty		
old, ancient		
little, tiny		

9. Unscramble the sentence and replace of the word "up"with the antonym "down".

Went the balloon up.

10. Find the words that are similar in meaning. Write the pairs of words in ABC order.

animal

creature

huge

gigantic

Name: ______________________ Date: ______________

Chapter 4

Lesson 23: Usage of words

You can scan the QR code given below or use the url to access additional EdSearch resources including videos and mobile apps related to *Usage of words*.

edSearch ***Usage of words***

URL	QR Code
http://www.lumoslearning.com/a/l25a	

Name: ______________________ Date: ______________

1. **We use or think of words that tell about real-life things that we know or happen to us.**

Read the words, then match them to the clue words in the box.

	bright, colorful half-circle in the sky, pot of gold	baby dog, cute 4-legged pet	desktop, laptop, technology tool	buddy, pal, companion
friend				
computer				
puppy				
rainbow				

2. **Read the words and sentences below. Choose the word that would best fit in the blank, given the real-life hints after each sentence. Use each word only one time.**

(shout, recess, laugh, playground)

a. Most of the kids go to the ______________ on Saturday to have fun. **HINT**: slide, swing, equipment

b. He would ______________ so loud at the jokes, his face would turn red. **HINT**: chuckle, giggle

c. Jeff's favorite thing at school is ______________. **HINT**: friends, play, outside, games

d. My ears hurt every time I hear her ______________! **HINT**: scream, yell, holler

3. **Some words fall into categories (real-life groups) of things we know well.**

Read the words and mark the best categories. Mark only 1 category for each word.

	Farm Animals	Indoor Pet Animals	Wild or Jungle Animals
cow			
dog			
horse			
elephant			
chicken			
lion			
hamster			
giraffe			
bear			

4. **Read the words below and choose the ones that describe a stuffed animal. Mark your answer.**

Ⓐ hard, prickly, rough
Ⓑ soft, cuddly, huggable

5. **People use transportation vehicles to get from one place to another. Read the words and Mark the transportation vehicle words.**

Ⓐ motorcycle
Ⓑ car
Ⓒ truck
Ⓓ train
Ⓔ tire
Ⓕ subway
Ⓖ wheel

6. **Some people live in apartments, houses, condos, trailers, motels and other places. In most living places there are kitchens- where food is cooked, living rooms- where people sit, visit or watch TV, and bedrooms- where people sleep. Read the words below and decide if the things belong in the kitchen, living room or bedroom. Write the correct words by each.**

word	places
stove	
couch	
chest of drawers	
refrigerator	
sink	
dresser	
recliner	
bed	
TV	

7. **Family members are a well-known real-life group. Read the words below. Mark the words that are in the group of family members.**

Ⓐ Farmer
Ⓑ Dentist
Ⓒ Uncle
Ⓓ Cousin
Ⓔ Mother
Ⓕ Mechanic
Ⓖ Daughter
Ⓗ Son
Ⓘ Teacher
Ⓙ Grandmother
Ⓚ Dad
Ⓛ Sister

8. **Words we use help us to picture them in our mind. The words below help us to picture things in our mind. Mark the words that help you to picture how a peppery hamburger should taste.**

Ⓐ Mouth-watering, juicy, delicious, spicy
Ⓑ Old, tart, dry, uncooked

9. **A category (group) of sports words are listed below. Choose the ones that match the sentences. Write them in the blanks.**

tennis

baseball

football

soccer

a. Freddie and Jeremiah played ______________ with their rackets.

b. When a goal is made in ______________, the ball is kicked into the net.

c. You use a bat in ______________.

d. Touchdowns are made in ______________.

10. Colors can be related to another color that have that color in it. Choose the color words (shades) that are alike.

Ⓐ Blue, sky blue, navy
Ⓑ Red, scarlet, candy apple
Ⓒ Orange, purple, green
Ⓓ Black, white, pink

Chapter 4

Lesson 24: Shades of Word Meanings

You can scan the QR code given below or use the url to access additional EdSearch resources including videos and mobile apps related to *Shades of Word Meanings*.

URL	QR Code
http://www.lumoslearning.com/a/l25b	

Name: ______________________ Date: ______________

1. **Verbs describe actions. The list below has verbs in it that are similar (related) to each other.**

   Choose the verbs that would describe what you could do with a ball. Mark your answer.

   Ⓐ eat, drink, smack, drool, sip, slurp
   Ⓑ toss, drop, throw, hurl, pitch, bounce

2. **Read the list of related verbs and match them to another verb that is like them in the box.**

   (neat, cry, sleepy, speak)

chat, talk	
tired, drowsy	
weep, sob	
tidy, clean	

3. **Read the sentence below and replace the underlined related verbs with one of the matching verbs.**

   We could not believe that he could <u>leap, spring</u> so high in the air.

   fall jump

   We could not believe that he could jump so high in the air.

   We could not believe that he could ______________ so high in the air.

4. **Read the sentences below. Mark the one that uses a verb related to laugh.**

Ⓐ They cried when the puppy was hurt.
Ⓑ She giggled when she saw the funny face on the clown.
Ⓒ He wanted to slurp his drink.
Ⓓ The teacher was happy with the good work her class did.

5. **Read the sentence below. Find the verb that is related to shouted and write it.**

The angry man yelled at the kids when they walked on his grass.

6. **Read the list of verbs below. Mark the pair that shows verbs that are NOT related.**

Ⓐ climb, go up
Ⓑ ran, sped
Ⓒ work, play
Ⓓ excited, thrilled

7. **Adjectives can be related (similar) to other adjectives. Read the list of adjective and match them in the box to like adjectives.**

	hilarious	slender	beautiful	overweight
thin, skinny				
fat, plump				
pretty, gorgeous				
silly, funny				

8. **Read the list of related adjectives. Choose the adjectives that would help to describe the weather.**

Ⓐ terrifying, scary, frightening
Ⓑ glamorous, gorgeous, beautiful
Ⓒ freezing, cold, frosty

9. **Read the sentence below. Find the adjective that is related to good and write it.**

The boys did an excellent job on their project.

10. **Read the sentences below and mark the 2 that use adjectives related to the adjective-main.**

Ⓐ The important information is in the first paragraph.
Ⓑ The last information is in the first paragraph.
Ⓒ The little information is in the first paragraph.
Ⓓ The major information is in the first paragraph.

Name: ______________________ Date: ______________

Chapter 4

Lesson 25: Vocabulary Acquisition

You can scan the QR code given below or use the url to access additional EdSearch resources including videos and mobile apps related to *Vocabulary Acquisition*.

URL	QR Code
http://www.lumoslearning.com/a/l26	

Name: ______________________ Date: ______________

Read the conversation below. Answer the questions about the words. Remember that adjectives describe nouns, verbs tell action, and adverbs help the verb.

George <u>said</u>, "Let's go on a hike in the <u>deep</u> woods today!"

"No way!" <u>shouted</u> Timothy. "I am <u>frightened</u> of the <u>dark</u> woods."

"Don't be <u>scared</u>!" George <u>replied</u>. "We'll take my <u>guard</u> dog with us. Smokey is a <u>great watch</u> dog. He will keep us safe from <u>harm</u>."

1. Which words describe the woods? Write them.

2. Which words tell about being afraid? Write them.

3. Which words below tell how George and Timothy talked? Mark 3 words from the story.

Ⓐ answered
Ⓑ spoke
Ⓒ replied
Ⓓ said
Ⓔ shouted

4. Use the words below and write a conversation between you and a friend. Be sure to use quotation marks, capital letters, and punctuation correctly.

bright sunlight

wonderful playground

joyfully swinging

Verbs, adverbs and adjectives may be used to help you understand words and phrases in reading. Read the story below and answer the question no 5 & 6.

Sally and her sister love to build sandcastles when they go to the sandy seashore. Their parents watch them play. They are happy when they see the girls happy.
The girls like to play in the waves, too. They dive deep in the waves, diving in and out of the surf. Their little brother, Tony, has the best time looking for shells. He grins when he sees his sisters grinning at him as he finds more shells.

5. Which sentence below from the story describes how the girls' parents feel?

Ⓐ The girls like to play in the waves, too.
Ⓑ Their parents watch them play.
Ⓒ They are happy when they see the girls happy.
Ⓓ Their little brother, Tony, has the best time looking for shells.

6. Which word in the following sentences tells about the girls' and brother's actions that are the same?

Ⓐ The girls like to play in the waves, too.
Ⓑ They dive deep in the waves, diving in and out of the surf.
Ⓒ Their little brother, Tony, has the best time looking for shells.
Ⓓ He grins when he sees his sisters grinning at him as he finds more shells.

Read the text and answer the questions relating to phrases using adverbs and adjectives.

My dog, Hattie May, is an <u>active adorable</u> Labrador Retriever. She chases her ball <u>wildly</u>, and <u>most always</u> catches it. Hattie May is <u>energetic</u> and <u>friendly</u> behaving in an outgoing manner.

She is a <u>typical gentle</u> dog with <u>loyalty</u> to me as her owner. My dog is kind and does not bite. She comes to me when I call her, follows me wherever I go, and stays by me when we are outside. Hattie is <u>obedient</u> and <u>intelligent</u>. You can tell her basic commands and she knows what to do.

7. Which words below describe Hattie May? Mark all that apply.

Ⓐ active adorable
Ⓑ disobedient
Ⓒ inside
Ⓓ outside
Ⓔ energetic
Ⓕ friendly
Ⓖ typical gentle
Ⓗ bites

8. Which sentences below tell how Hattie is obedient and intelligent?

Ⓐ She is a typical gentle dog with loyalty to me as her owner.
Ⓑ She comes to me when I call her, follows me wherever I go, and stays by me when we are outside.
Ⓒ You can tell her basic commands and she knows what to do.
Ⓓ Hattie May is energetic and friendly behaving in an outgoing manner.

9. Read the following text and decide which sentence does NOT support the information.

Washing a car is important. Not only does the car look better, but by washing it the paint job stays on longer and won't chip as easily.

When you wash a car, be sure to use a car wash product or a soft soap mixture with water. Soak the car with clean water first, then apply the car wash product or soap solution. Using a sponge or soft cloth wash the car in circular motions. Rinse periodically and repeat until the car is clean.

Ⓐ Cars do not need to be washed.
Ⓑ Washing a car helps the paint job stay on longer.
Ⓒ Soak the car with clean water first.
Ⓓ Rinse periodically and repeat.

10. Unscramble the sentence to make sense using the phrases. Start your sentence with – The lazy cat- as the subject.

On the soft velvet couch in the sunny afternoon The lazy cat slept

End of Language

Answer Key and Detailed Explanations

Chapter 4: Language

Lesson 1: People, Places, and Things

Question No.	Answer	Detailed Explanations
1	-	The correct collective nouns are flock, litter, swarm, and pack. These words describe the group of things in each sentence.
2	-	herd, bunch, flock, swarm
3	A, D	The correct answers are- We looked for the deck of cards, and There was a colony of ants in our garden. These are the only sentences with collective nouns in them.
4	A	The phrase that does NOT have a collective noun in it is the first phrase- ran to the store. It is the correct answer. The other phrases all have collective nouns in them- band, bundle, and bunch. They are incorrect.
5	D	The only collective noun that makes sense in the sentence is bundle. It is correct. Joshua carried a bundle of firewood to the house.
6	-	The correct way to unscramble the words will make these words in this order- swarm, pride, flock, and colony. These are the correct answers.
7	-	To make the paragraph correct, the following words need to be inserted to the sentences in this order-bouquet, pod, and school. This is the only correct order.
8	-	The best examples are bundle for sticks, herd for buffalo, litter for puppies, and pride for lion.
9	A, C, D	The correct answers are the first sentence- Maryann was excited to see the herd of buffalos at Yellowstone National Park, the third sentence- The band of soldiers fought hard in the battle, and the fourth sentence- He could not believe the swarm of bees that came out of the hive. The second sentence is not correct as it does not have a collective noun in it.
9.1	-	The correct words are herd from the first sentence, band from the second sentence, and swarm from the third sentence. They may be in any order.
10	-	Answers will vary but must include the collective noun "litter" as that is what relates to a group of kittens or puppies.

Lesson 2: Language conventions

Question No.	Answer	Detailed Explanations
1	-	The words should be marked as follows- elephant and slipper are nouns, as they name things; little and fuzzy are adjectives, as they tell about the nouns; walking and running are verbs, as they tell actions; and really and quickly are adverbs, as they tell more about the verbs. These are the correct answers.
2	B, C	A complete sentence must have a subject and a predicate. The first and fourth sentences do not have subjects. They are not correct. The second and third sentences are correct. They both have subjects and predicates. Margie and I love to go hiking in the woods. Tracy is happy that he has a new little baby brother.
3	-	The first phrase-ran a long way home is missing a subject, the second phrase- My friends and I is missing a predicate, the third phrase- Grandma and Grandpa is missing a predicate and the fourth phrase- skipping in the rain is missing a subject. These are the only correct answers.
4	-	To use each verb one time, the only correct answers are- a. draw, b. follow, c. ran, d. bake, e. see.
5	-	The correct compound sentence should be – Jamar had a party and all his friends came to it. This is the only correct answer.
6	-	In each of these sentences, the subject pronoun is found as the first word in the sentence and should be Underlined. These are the only correct answers, She, It, He, You, I, We, and They.
7	-	The correct answers are her, us, and him. They are the only object pronouns in the sentences.

Question No.	Answer	Detailed Explanations
8	-	**Subjects** The older man Skippy Mel and Tom Valerie **Predicates** made a funny face was the best puppy I ever had are great friends will be 8 years old in 2 weeks
9	-	The adjectives in the sentences that describe the nouns are beautiful, curious, shy and healthy. These are the only correct answers and should be underlined.
10	-	The correct subjects name a person, place or thing in the sentences. a. The big dogs is correct. Running around does not make sense and does not name anything. b. Daddy is correct. Walking does not make sense and does not name anything. c. The red bird is correct. Faster does not make sense and does not name anything. d. A flower garden is correct. Raining does not make sense and does not name anything. e. Tree branches is correct. Skating does not make sense and does not name anything.

Lesson 3: Regular & Irregular Plural Nouns

Question No.	Answer	Detailed Explanations
1	-	By changing the "f" in each word to a "v" and adding "es" the following words are correct- wolves, shelves, leaves, knives, and elves.
2	-	By changing the "y" to "i" and adding "es", the new plural words are butterflies, flies, stories, and babies. These are the only correct words.
3	-	The correct matches for singular to plural are box to boxes, bench to benches, wish to wishes, tomato to tomatoes, and potato to potatoes.
4	-	The correct plurals for each sentence are mice, people, geese, and feet. The other choices are not the correct plural form of the nouns.
5	-	The correct matches are child to children, woman to women, and man to men. These are the only correct answers.
6	-	The correct word changes are cat to cats- add "s", dice to die- change to new word, dress to dresses- add "es", tooth to teeth- change word to new word, table to tables- add "s".
7	-	Answers will vary, but must include the plural form of leaf, leaves in the sentence.
8	B, C, D	The first sentence is not correct, as the noun cow was changed to cows to be plural. The second, third and fourth sentences are correct, as the nouns deer, buffalo and sheep do not change from singular to plural.
9	-	The 3 plural words in the sentence are families, babies, and woods. These nouns mean more than one and are correct. They should be unferlined.
10	-	a. The correct answer is children, as it is plural and is the only one that makes sense. b. The correct answer is classes, as it is plural and is the only one that makes sense. c. The correct answer is trucks, as it is plural and makes sense. The other answers are not plural and do not make sense in the sentences.

Lesson 4: Reflexive pronouns

Question No.	Answer	Detailed Explanations
1	-	The reflexive pronouns in each sentence are themselves, myself, herself, and ourselves. These are the only correct answers.
2	-	The correct answers are for sentence #1 subject is I and reflexive pronoun is myself, sentence #2 subject is She and reflexive pronoun is herself, sentence #3 subject is We and reflexive pronoun is ourselves.
3	-	The correct answer choices are: a. ourselves, as it reflects the subject We. b. herself as it reflects the subject She. c. themselves as it reflects the subject They. d. himself as it reflects the subject He. These are the only correct answer choices.
4	B	The sentence that does NOT have a reflexive pronoun is the second sentence- Sarah and Tammy played the piano. The other sentences all have reflexive pronouns himself, himself, and themselves.
5	C	The correct answer is yourself, as it reflects you in the sentence. The other answers do not and are not correct.
6	-	They did it themselves. - the correct order for the sentence. They is the subject and themselves is the correct pronoun.
7	-	To use the reflexive nouns correctly, the only correct answers are I to make the sentence "I am cooking it myself." He to make the sentence "He fixed himself a sandwich." We to make "We wanted to paint the doghouse ourselves." You to make "You shouldn't go out by yourself in the dark."
8	A, D	The sentences that use reflexive pronouns correctly are the first and fourth sentences. Robert cut himself by accident and They made themselves soda floats. The second and third sentences are not correct, as they do not use the correct reflexive pronouns.
9	A, B	The first sentence, "The monkey likes to rub itself against the door." - correct. The second sentence, "The kitten often licks itself to get clean." - the second correct sentence. The third and fourth sentences do not make sense and are not the correct use of the reflexive pronoun "itself".
10	-	Answers will vary but must include I as the subject and myself as the reflexive pronoun.

Lesson 5: Past tense of verbs

Question No.	Answer	Detailed Explanations
1	B, D	The correct sentences that give information about what verbs do in a sentence are the second and fourth sentences. Verbs tell the action in a sentence. Verbs are a part of the predicate. The first and third sentences are not correct.
2	-	Using the text on irregular verbs, the following is the only correct answer- verb is changed to a new word or stays the same in present and past tense.
3	A, D, F, G	The correct past tense irregular verbs in the list are: sat, ate, hid, and told. The others are present tense verbs.
4	-	The correct past tense irregular verbs for the sentences are a. ran b. went c. saw d. taught
5	-	The correct matches for the present and past tense verbs are draw-drew, take-took, know-knew, come-came, meet-met, find-found and drink-drank. These are the only correct answers.
6	-	went; found; made; ate; swam
7	D	The fourth sentence is the only correct answer. I hide from my big brother is present tense, not past. The other sentences all use past tense irregular verbs and are not correct.
8	A, B, C	The verbs that have present tense and past tense irregular verbs are fly-flew, hear-heard, and sleep-slept. They must be underlined. Play-played and walk-walked are not correct as they do not have irregular past tenses.
9	-	The correct answers are read, let, cut, and quit. These verbs do not change from present to past tense.
10	-	The correct matches are stand-stood, drive-drove, grow-grew, fall-fell, choose-chose, and freeze-froze. These are the only correct answers.

Name: ______________________ Date: ______________

Lesson 6: Simple and compound sentences

Question No.	Answer	Detailed Explanations
1	-	The phrases that are not complete sentences are "Mary and Jane want. to go to the store" and "Mary asked her mother. for some money." The other sentences are complete and have both subjects and verbs.
1.1	-	The correct sentences must be- Mary and Jane want to go to the store. Mary asked her mother for some money. These are the only correct answers.
2	-	The complete sentences from the story are- They got ready. Her mother gave her $2. Jane got $5 from her dad. These are the only correct answers but may be in any order.
3	-	The correct matches are- the beautiful ponies were fun to ride, Roberto and Miguel love to play football, The chicken soup was good to eat, and She brushed her hair. No other answers are correct.
4	-	The correct matches are sped down the hill to The racecar, rode her bike up the road to Betty, started ringing when the fire began to alarm, and broke as it fell to the floor to The dish. These are the only right answers because the question states that each can only be used one time.
5	-	The correct answers are- Their mother bought the pumpkins, and everyone helped carve funny faces on them. - Joshua and Kevin planted pumpkin seeds, and Mom watered the garden. - They tended the garden, so the plants grew bigger. - Finally, the vines had blooms and little pumpkins started to form. They are compounded sentences, because they have 2 complete simple sentences and are combined with a conjunction.
6	B, C	The second and third sentences are compound sentences as they have 2 simple sentences put together. Sammy wanted to learn archery, so he took lessons. The monkeys climbed the trees and chimpanzees swung from branches. They are correct. The other 2 sentences are simple sentences and are not correct.
7	-	The correct compound sentence is- The pecan tree branches were blowing in the wind, but the rose bushes stood still. This is the best correct combination.

Question No.	Answer	Detailed Explanations
8	-	a. Teachers work hard, so the students can learn. b. People ride to work on the bus, because they do not want to drive. c. I like to eat pizza, but Tommy likes hamburgers. The correct conjunctions are "so" for Teachers work hard, __ the students can learn. – "because" for People ride to work on the bus, ______ they do not want to drive. – "but" for I like to eat pizza, ____ Tommy likes hamburgers. These are the only conjunctions that make the simple sentences into compound sentences.
9	C	The sentence that is NOT compound is the third answer. They found the little skinny dog in their backyard. It is the only one that has only 1 subject and 1 predicate. The first, second and fourth sentences have 2 subjects and predicates and are compound sentences. They are not correct.

Name: ______________________ Date: ______________

Lesson 7: Understand Language conventions

Question No.	Answer	Detailed Explanations
1	-	The correct proper nouns in the sentences are 1. Sarah, 2. Dallas, Texas, 3. Valentine's Day, and 4. John, Skipper, Saturday. These all must be underlined as they name particular people, places, holidays, and days of the week.
2	-	The words that should be capitalized and name a particular product are Cheerios cereal, Skippy peanut butter, and Kraft cheese. The word popcorn should not be capitalized as it does not name a particular product brand.
3	A, C, D	The correct answers are the first, third and fourth choices. Dear Mayor, - Dearest Grandma, - and Respectfully, - they use the comma correctly. The second answer does not use the comma correctly, as it should be after you – not after Thank. It is not correct.
4	-	a. should not = shouldn't b. is not = isn't c. did not = didn't
5	A, C, E	The words that correctly show possession are Mike's, Jess', and Martha's. The ones that are not correct are Daniels, and Cammies, as they do not have the apostrophe mark after the name before the letter "s".
6	-	The words that follow rule #1 are boil and toil. The words that follow rule #2 are toy and coy. These are the only correct answers.
7	-	The words with "dge" are badge, fudge, and bridge. The words with "ge" are age, rage, page, and stage. These are the only correct answers.
8	A	The best answer would be the dictionary, as it would give information about how to use the word and its pronunciation.
9	-	Answers will vary, but must include that yes, the word Monday would fall on this page. The reason is that in ABC order, Monday would come between the word man and before the word monster. This can be written in a different way, but must be included.
10	-	The words which must be capitalized are Mary, Halloween, and Friday. They are proper nouns. The words- stamps and tomorrow should not as they are not proper nouns.

Lesson 8: How is it Capitalized?

Question No.	Answer	Detailed Explanations
1	A, C, D	The correct answers are Easter, Memorial Day, Valentine's Day. They are holidays. Eggs and Presents are not correct as they are not holidays.
2	B	The correct sentence is- Mary and her mother made cupcakes for Veteran's Day. The other sentences have holidays in them, but they are not correct as they are not capitalized.
3	brand	The words that should be capitalized and marked in the box are Ford, Amazon, M & M's, and Coca Cola. They are product brand names. The other words truck, dog food, candy and store are not product names and should be marked do not capitalize.
4	A, B	The 2 sentences that use product brand names correctly are- Most people like to eat Lay's chips. – He drove a bright shiny Toyota truck. The other sentences have product names, but they are not brand names and are not capitalized, so they are not correct.
5	-	The sentence should be rewritten as follows- His brother drove a Chevrolet 4x4 truck, but his mom liked her Buick car better. This is the only correct answer, as Chevrolet and Buick must be capitalized.
6	-	The correct answers are Main Street- Dallas, Texas- Japan-Yellowstone National Park. These must be capitalized as they are names of places.
7	-	The words that should be underlined are Hawaii, Washington Avenue, England and Target as they are names of places and must be capitalized.
8	-	The words that need to be capitalized are Walmart, Sears, Disneyworld, and Chicago, Illinois. The words big highway and tiny store are not names of particular places and should not be capitalized.
9	C	The sentence that does NOT have the correct use of capitalization of names of places is the third sentence. The train stopped in biloxi, mississippi. Biloxi, Mississippi must be capitalized. This is the only correct answer as the other sentences use correct capitalization.
10	-	Answers will vary but must make sense and be written in a sentence that is correct. The name of the place, San Francisco, California must be in the sentence.

Lesson 9: The Comma and Quotation Dilemma

Question No.	Answer	Detailed Explanations
1	A, C, D	The correct answers are Dear Calvin, - Dearest Grandmother, - To Whom It May Concern, - the other answers are not correct as they do not use the comma at the end of the salutation.
2	-	The corrections should be that a comma is added after Daddy and after again. These are the only correct answers.
3	D	The only correct answer is Dear Aunt Bea, as it has the correct use of the comma. The other answers are not correct as they do not have the comma placed at the end of the salutation.
4	-	The salutations that should be fixed are To the President, and Dear Eddie, - the others have the correct use of the comma. These are the only correct answers.
5	-	The salutations are Dear Greg, - Dearest Cousin Ida, - Dear Jasmine, the others Respectfully, and Thanks, are closings. These are the only correct way to mark them.
6	-	The second letter should be underlined as it has the correct use of the comma in both the salutation and closing. Dear Katy, and Your friend forever, - the first letter is not correct as it is missing the comma in the closing.
7	-	The correct answers are: Yours truly - Yours truly, Thanks - Thanks, Best regards - Best regards, Yours faithfully - Yours faithfully, Always - Always, these are the only answers.
8	A	The best salutation for the letter is the first one- Dear Uncle Joseph, as it is stated in the letter that it is to her uncle. It is correct and should be highlighted. The other answers are not correct.
9	D	The best closing would be Yours always, as it shows a personal relationship. The other answers do not and are not correct.
10	C	The best answer for a closing for a letter to a mayor would be Respectfully, as it shows no personal relationship. The other answers are not correct as they show a close friendship.

Lesson 10: Use an apostrophe

Question No.	Answer	Detailed Explanations
1	-	Following the rules given in the information, taking out the "a" in "are" and replacing it with an ' and taking out the "i" in "is" and replacing it with an ' make the new contractions. The correct contractions to make are' they're, we're, she's, he's, and you're. These are the only answers.
2	B, C	The two sentences that have contractions in them are – We aren't going to go shopping until Friday. They're happy to go on vacation. They are the correct answers. The other sentences do not have contractions in them and are not correct.
3	-	The correct answers are -aren't, haven't, didn't, and isn't. They are the only answers when the not is the second word and the letter "o" is left out and 'put in its place.
4	C	The only correct answer is the third sentence. The firemen won't let the fire spread. It has the contraction "won't" in it for will not.
5	-	a. the correct contraction is "aren't" (are not) as it makes sense in the sentence. The contraction "can't" does not make sense and is not correct. b. the correct contraction is "isn't" (is not) as it makes sense. The contraction "didn't" does not make sense and is not correct. c. the correct contraction is "Let's" (Let us) as it makes sense. The contraction "You've" does not make sense and is not correct. d. the correct contraction is "she'd" (she had) as it makes sense in the sentence. The contraction "I'm" does not make sense and is not correct.
6	-	The correct answers are Manuel's, Tony's, Bess', Emanuel's, Mr. Brown's, and Ms. Bliss'. The words must be made possessive by adding 's unless they end in "s" and then only add '.
7	A, D, E	The groups of words that do NOT show possession are – Large dresses, Fancy hats, and Spicy cheeseburgers. They are correct answers. The other groups of words do show possession and are not correct.
8	B, C	The second and third sentences use possessive nouns correctly. My sister's room is a mess. He listens to Brad's music all the time. The first and fourth sentences do not have ' before the s and are not correct.
9	-	The correct order of the sentence is- Patty's mother let her keep the tiny kitten. This is the only order of words for this sentence.

Question No.	Answer	Detailed Explanations
10	-	The correct answers are Mary's, Vicky's, Vicky's, and girls'. These are the only possessives in the story. Vicky's should be highlighted both times it appears.

Lesson 11: Spelling patterns

Question No.	Answer	Detailed Explanations
1	B, C, D, E	The correct answers are the words back, rack, stick, and flick. They have a short vowel and end in the "k" sound spelled "ck". The other words do not follow the rule and are not correct.
2	-	The words that should be marked YES are play, stay, and away. They follow the rule of "ay" at the end of the word. The words that should be marked NO are bake and story. These do not follow the rule.
3	-	The words with long "e" are We, tree in sentence 1, eat, piece in sentence 2, Please in sentence 3, and freeze in sentence 4. These are the only correct answers that follow the long "e" rules.
4	B, D, E	The correct answers are Beef, Sleep, and Meat. They follow the long "e" patterns. The other words are short "e" and are not correct.
5	-	The words that should have long o written next to them are boat, smoke, coat and float. These follow the long o spelling patterns. The words that should have short o next to them are stop, and logs.
6	-	The correct answers that use the long o spelling pattern and make sense in the sentences are floated, coats, goats, and broke. These are the only correct answers.
7	A, B, E	The correct answers that match the spelling pattern long "a" as in "ai" are train, afraid, and mail. The other words are short a and are not correct.
8	D	The correct answer is the fourth sentence- They will follow the directions given. It is the only sentence that does NOT follow the spelling pattern. The other sentences all have words in them that follow the "oi" spelling pattern. They are not correct.
9	-	We found the boy in the woods.
10	-	The words that follow the long e, 2-syllable pattern where the first syllable has a long e are secret, depend, and even. The word that does not follow the pattern is settle. These are the only correct answers.

Lesson 12: Consult reference materials

Question No.	Answer	Detailed Explanations
1	B	The guide words that would be on the top of the page in a dictionary where the word – giraffe- would be found are - "germ great". The word giraffe would fall between these words in ABC order. The second answer is correct. It would not with the other guide words. They are not correct.
2	B	The correct answer is -Excited- eager, enthusiastic, anticipating emotions. This is the only correct answer. The other definitions of words- explosive, and skinny- do not make sense in the sentence.
3	B,C	The 2 words that are not spelled correctly and need to be looked up in the dictionary to correct the spelling are- forgeting, and childran. They should be marked. The other words- happy and complete are spelled correctly and do not need to be checked.
4	B, C, E	The topics that would be found in an online encyclopedia are -Rainforest, Trees, and Cats. They are correct. The words funny and walking might not be in an online encyclopedia or would not contain as much information and are not correct.
5	-	The correct ABC order is mean, missing, mistake, money, multiply. This is the only correct order done by second and third letter ABC order.
6	-	The word that was used too many times is – likes. It is the only correct answer.
7	-	The words that have the correct synonyms are happy and ran. The word ate does not match fixed, corrected and is not correct.
8	A, B, D	The words that are antonyms are- happy, sad- many, few- on, off. They are correct. The words- begin, start are not antonyms and are not correct.
9	A, D	The words that must be highlighted in the first list are butiful and frutful as they are not spelled correctly in the first list and are in the second list.
10	-	The correct answers are a. Atlas, b. Dictionary, c. Encyclopedia and d. Thesaurus as they match the definitions given.

Lesson 13: Use knowledge of language and its conventions

Question No.	Answer	Detailed Explanations
1	C	The story setting is at Noe's house. That is the only correct answer. The other answers are not found and are not correct.
2	-	The characters in the story are Noe and Kevin. They can be listed in any order to be correct.
3	-	Answers will vary but must include that the problem was the boys needed to fill with air the tires on their bikes.
4	A, B	The best ideas would be the first and second sentences. You could get the materials and make the sandwich while you were talking about it. You could pass out notes to the class, so they could follow along. The other sentences would not be correct.
5	D	You would NOT want to -Look down at the floor while speaking. The fourth answer is the best. The other answers are things that you would want to do and are not correct.
6	A, B, D	The sentences that follow the story are the first, second and fourth. Pets can keep you company. Pets can learn tricks. Kids like to have pets. They are correct. The third sentence does not follow the story and is not correct.
7	B	The correct answer is the second sentence. The story does not talk about feeding your pet. That is why it does NOT follow the story.
8	-	Answers will vary but should include one of the following- kids like pets, they can keep them company, and can be taught to do tricks. All acceptable answers will count.
9	A, C	The 2 sentences that help you be a good listener are the first and third sentences. Keep your eyes on the speaker. Take notes to help you remember what they said. The second and fourth sentences are not good listening habits and are not correct.
10	-	The first and third sentences show good listening- Pay attention to the speaker. Show interest or ask questions afterwards. The second sentence shows not good listening. Read a book. These are the only correct markings.

Lesson 14: Formal and Informal language

Question No.	Answer	Detailed Explanations
1	-	The informal names are Mother, Classmate, Best Friend, and Grandma. The formal names are Mayor, and President. These are the only correct answers.
2	-	The correct answers are a. informal (talking to a friend), b. formal (invite to a judge), c. formal (formal invitation), d. informal (friends), e. formal (speaking to the President). These are the only correct answers.
3	A, D	The 2 sentences that show informal use of English are "Mom, I am hungry!" and "Yeah, we won the game!" They are correct. The other 2 sentences are formal use and are not correct.
4	-	Formal
4.1	-	Answers will vary but should include that it would be formal because the student does not know the people personally.
5	B	The best answer to show formal English is the second sentence. "We had a good time visiting the zoo today." The first and third sentences are not correct as they are written in informal English.
6	-	The sentence that shows informal use of English is- Suddenly, Sara shouted, "Wow! Check out this painting of a zebra!" This is the only sentence in the story that shows a personal relationship. It is correct.
7	-	The correct answer is "Please help me get on the elevator." By removing the word "Hey", the sentence changes from informal to formal. Be sure that the student answer has the correct capitalization and punctuation.
8	C, B, A	The correct order of the sentences is- We wanted to thank you for helping our students with their projects on crime prevention. You were very thoughtful and kind. Thanks again for all you do in our city. This is the only order that makes sense for this formal letter.
9	B, A, C	The best order of the sentences for this informal letter is- Hey, Unc! Thanks for the super surprise that I got in the mail. I had always wanted my own pair of skates! Looking forward to seeing you next week! -This is the only correct answer.
10	-	Answers will vary but should include words to show that the student knows Jerome personally.

Lesson 15: Same Word Different Meanings

Question No.	Answer	Detailed Explanations
1	B	The second answer is correct as the word "second" in the story means what comes after first.
2	A	The first answer is correct as the word "bat" in the story means a piece of baseball equipment.
3	B	The correct answer is the second sentence- Eddie heard the ball whizzing by him. This sentence helps you imagine the sound of the ball going by him. The first and third sentences do not relate to the sound of the ball and are not correct.
4	-	The correct matches are fly- a ball caught after being hit in a baseball game, hand- a body part with fingers and a thumb on it, and ear- a body part used to hear with. The other definitions do not match with the story and are not correct.
5	B	The correct answer is the second one- A simile that compares her eating to that of a balloon with too much air in it.
6	A, C, D	The correct answers are the first, third and fourth sentences. Mrs. Jones' classroom was a zoo. Time is money. The van was a heater in the summer afternoon. They contain metaphors. The second sentence is not correct as it contains a simile.
7	B	The best answer for schedule is the second one- to plan. The other answers are not the meaning of schedule in the story and are not correct.
8	C	The best answer for dismissed is the third one- stopped or released. The other answers are not the meaning of dismissed in the story and are not correct.
9	B	The second sentence is correct. Due to the heat of the day, students have a break after lunch, so they do not get heat exhaustion. It explains why they take a break after lunch. The first sentence does not explain why and is not correct.
10	A	The first sentence explains which students participate. It is correct. They all play the games and do the activities. The other sentence does not explain which students participate and is not correct.

Lesson 16: Prefix and Suffix

Question No.	Answer	Detailed Explanations
1	-	The correct answers are a. unhappy- not happy, b. unopened- not opened, c. unable- not able, d. unknown- not known. There are no other answers.
2	B	-
3	-	The correct answers are a. reread- read again, b. replay – play again, c. redo – do again. There are no other answers.
4	-	The first sentence has the word "preschool" in it and should be underlined. The second sentence has the word "preheat" in it and should be highlighted. These are the only correct answers.
5	-	The prefix "bi" means two and the prefix "tri" means three. These are the only correct answers.
6	C	The third sentence does NOT have a prefix in it and is the correct answer. She was very happy and excited to see her aunt.
7	-	The correct order of letters in the words must be unhappy, preschool, reread, and dislike. These are the only correct answers.
8	A, D	The sentences that have prefix words in them are- He didn't preview the music before he played. The word preview has the prefix- pre. It is unlikely that I passed that test. The word unlikely has the prefix -un. These are the only correct answers. The other sentences do not have prefixes in any words.
9	-	The words that have a prefix added are preview and unkind. They should be marked. The other words ringing and lived are not correct as they do not have prefixes in them.
10	-	The correct answers are 1. b- not cooked for uncooked, 2. c- watched before others for preview, 3. d- do again for repeat. These are the only correct answers.

Lesson 17: Adjectives and adverbs

Question No.	Answer	Detailed Explanations
1	-	The correct adjectives are purple, second-grade, yellow bright, funny, grumpy old, and good. They tell about each of the nouns in the phrases.
2	A	The first sentence has 3 adjectives in it. The pretty little lady was looking for her tiny kitten. The first sentence is correct. The other sentences have adverbs and do not have 3 adjectives.
3	C	The adjective that makes sense in the sentence is fluffy. It is the only correct answer. The words loudly, and well are adverbs and do not make sense. The words first-grade are adjectives, but do not make sense. They are incorrect.
4	-	The correct adjectives are good, huge, orange, and sweet. The other words are not adjectives and do not make sense. They are not correct.
5	-	The correct matches are white shiny diamond, giant squawking parrot, brown wooden chest, and green prickly cactus. These are the best answers.
6	B	The correct answer is the second sentence. She quietly went to her room to study. The word "quietly" is the adverb. The other sentences are not correct.
7	B, E, F, G	The adverbs are slowly, very, well, and gladly. They can modify verbs, adverbs or another adjective. These are the correct answers. The other words pretty, beautiful and tiny are adjectives and tell about a noun. They are not correct.
8	-	The correct answers are well to modify how he did his work, proudly to modify how she walked, carefully to modify how he did the test and slowly to modify how the car stopped.
9	-	The adjectives are breakable and golden. They should be marked that way. The adverbs are correctly and silently and should be marked that way.
10	well, good	The correct answer to the first sentence is well, as the word is an adverb and modifies how they did. Good would be incorrect. The word good is correct in the second sentence as it is an adjective and describes the science projects. Well would be incorrect.

Lesson 18: The Context Clue

Question No.	Answer	Detailed Explanations
1	-	The words that should be underlined are broke, iron, and cave. Each word should be highlighted 2 times to be correct.
2	-	The correct answers are 1. handle, 2. mind, 3. stare, 4. flower, 5. mind, and 6. flour. These are the only correct answers.
3	-	The words that rhyme are scout with about, believe with relieve, sing with ring, and fox with box. These are the only correct answers.
4	-	The correct answers are piece, peace and knows, nose. These are the only answers where the words sound the same in each row and mean something different.
4.1	-	The correct answers for the sentences are piece, peace, nose, and knows. He wants a piece of cake. When the baby sleeps, we have peace and quiet. She has a pretty little nose. Callie knows all her multiplication facts. These are the only correct answers in this order.
5	-	The correct answers are stake, stake and weight, wait. These are the only answers where the words sound the same in each row and mean something different.
5.1	-	The correct answers are stake, steak, wait, and weight. Mr. Brown put a stake in the ground to mark the garden. Dad cooks steak on the outdoor grill. Mom said to wait to go swimming. The weight of the trunk was over 100 pounds. These are the only correct answers in this order.
6	-	The sentence that is correct is- He doesn't mind helping his sister with her homework. The other sentences do not make sense and are not correct.
7	-	The correct answers are hair, and hare. The hair of the fair princess was golden. The hare ran when the dogs chased him.
8	B	The correct answer is peace. It tells about things being calm, quiet, and happy.
9	-	The correct answers are – threw hard for hurled, and rude for curt. These are the only answers. The other answers do not follow the sentence thought and are not correct.
10	B, C, E	The correct answers are- huge, gigantic- cold, freezing- begin, start. They are synonyms. The other words are not and are not correct.

Lesson 19: Roots and Affixes

Question No.	Answer	Detailed Explanations
1	D	These are correct because they give the meaning of the underlined word in each sentence.
1.1	A	
1.2	B	
2	-	The correct answers are careful, hopeless, breakable, and thankful. These are the only words that can be made with the new endings added.
3	-	The correct answers are- able for comfortable, -less for hopeless, -ful for respectful, and -ful for playful. These are the only correct answers.
4	-	The correct root word for respectful, respected, and respects is respect. The correct root word for careless, careful, and caring is care. The correct root word for playful, played, and playing is play. The correct root word for breakable, breaking, and breaks is break. These are the only correct answers.
5	-	The correct answers are a. comfortable, b. appearance, c. playful, d. careful. These are the only answers that make sense in the sentences with the definitions given.
6	-	Answers will vary but must include the correct use of the word kindness to be correct.
7	-	The only correct order for the sentence is- It was careless of him to drop the trophy. No other combinations make sense.
8	-	The correct root words are- 1. respect (take off the ending ful), 2. care (take off the ending ful), 3. thank (take off the ending ful), and 4. mind (take off the ending ful). These are the only correct answers.
9	C	The only ending that can be added to the root word "care" and make sense in the sentence is "less". This is the correct answer to make the new word careless.
10	-	The correct order of letters in the words are artful, kindness, careful, appearance. These are the only correct answers.

Lesson 20:Connecting related words

Question No.	Answer	Detailed Explanations
1	-	The correct compound words are hamburger, popcorn, milkshake, butterfly and toothbrush. They must be in this order to be correct.
2	-	The correct compound words in ABC order are doorbell, football, homework and weekend. They must be in order to be correct.
3	-	Sentence 1- horseback is the correct answer to highlight. Sentence 2- skateboard is the correct answer to highlight. Sentence 3- Grandma is the correct answer to highlight. Sentence 4- Someone is the correct answer to highlight. Sentence 5- Watermelon is the correct answer to highlight. These are the compound words in the sentences.
4	C	The compound word that would be used if talking about something to carry books in is backpack. It is correct. The other compound words do not make sense or answer the questions.
5	-	The compound words are sidewalk and pancake. They should be marked in the "Compound word" column. The words walking and because are not compound words. They should be marked in the "Not a compound word" column.
6	-	The correct compound word answers are- a. birdhouse, b. snowman, c. highway, d. cheeseburger. No other answers are correct.
7	-	The compound words that belong in each sentence are a. outside, b. inside. These are the only correct answers.
8	-	The two words that need to be combined to make compound words in each sentence are- 1. base ball, 2. skate board, 3. straw berries, and 4. fish bowl.
8.1	-	The only correct answers are baseball, skateboard, strawberries and fishbowl in that order. They are the compound words that need to be in the sentences from number 8.
9	-	Answers will vary but must use the compound word "cupcake" correctly in a sentence.
10	-	The correct compound words are sunflower, moonlight, backyard, sailboat, and something. These are the only correct answers.

Lesson 21: Find the meaning

Question No.	Answer	Detailed Explanations
1	-	The definition of cooler in the sentence matches definition 2. That is the only correct answer as the word cooler is used as a noun in the sentence.
2	-	The correct answer is toupee as it makes sense in the sentence. The word troop does not make sense in the sentence and is not correct.
3	A, D, E, G	The words that would be on the dictionary page are now, nut, novel, and nuance. They would fall between the guide words nose and nutty in ABC order. They are the only correct answers. The words open, never and problem would not be on the page and are not correct.
4	D, E, G	The correct words that would NOT be found on this dictionary page between the guide words are deliver, every, and everything. They are the ones that must be highlighted. The other words would fall on the page and are not correct.
5	E	The correct answer is- amber- adj., dark orange or yellow color. Amber is used as an adjective in describing the color of a car. The other words have noun definitions and are not correct.
6	-	The correct answers are landmark and geographical. The well-known landmark helped the scientist find the geographical location. The other words do not make sense and are not correct.
7	E, G	The correct answers are monopolized and justify. He monopolized the meeting to justify his opinion. The other words do not make sense and are not correct.
8	-	The word from the glossary that means a type of bird is emu. That is the only correct answer.
9	C	The dictionary that would be best for students to use is Britannica Kids, https://kids.britannica.com. It is the correct answer. The other dictionaries would not be the best for students and would not be correct.
10	-	The correct answers are 3 for the first sentence in the box. He struck the match to light the campfire wood., 2 for the second sentence- They were a perfect match., and 1 for I played in the tennis match. These are the only correct answers that match the definitions.

Lesson 22: The meaning of words

Question No.	Answer	Detailed Explanations
1	-	The word that is weaker is afraid and the stronger word is frightened. This is the only correct answer as afraid gives a feeling of being scared, but frightened gives more of an emotion.
2	-	The correct answers for the sentences are- a. gorgeous as it is a more detailed meaning for very pretty- b. frightened as it is a more detailed meaning for very scared- c. awful as it is a more detailed meaning for very bad- d. gigantic as it is a more detailed meaning for very big. These are the only correct answers.
3	-	yes, play, closed, there
4	-	The correct word matches are hot to cold, happy to sad, short to tall, fast to slow, left to right and on to off. These are the only correct answers.
5	-	The correct answers are happy to happier and happiest, thin to thinner and thinnest, big to bigger and biggest, and angry to angrier and angriest. These are the only correct answers by using the rule given.
6	-	The correct answers are trash- garbage, happy-joyous, smart-brilliant, and looked-stared. These are the only correct words that make sense.
7	B	The second sentence- The icing on the cake was sugary tasting., -has the synonym sugary for sweet in it. It is the correct answer.
8	-	The answers are -antonyms, sweet, sour- clean, dirty. Synonyms-old, ancient- little, tiny. These are the correct answers.
9	-	The correct answer is- The balloon went down. This is the only correct way to unscramble the words and substitute the word "down" for "up".
10	-	The only correct answers are animal, creature and gigantic, huge. These pairs match in meaning and are in ABC order.

Lesson 23: Usage of words

Question No.	Answer	Detailed Explanations
1	-	The correct answers are rainbow to - bright, colorful half-circle in the sky, pot of gold; puppy to- baby dog, cute 4-legged pet; computer to- desktop, laptop, technology tool, and friend to- buddy, pal, companion. These are the only correct answers.
2	-	a. playground b. laugh c. recess d. shout
3	-	The words that must be marked farm animals are cow, horse, and chicken. The words that must be marked indoor pet animals are dog and hamster. The words that must be marked wild or jungle animals are elephant, lion, giraffe, and bear. These are the only correct answers.
4	B	The best answer is soft, cuddly, huggable. The other answer does not describe a stuffed animal. It is not correct.
5	A, B, C, D, F	The correct transportation vehicle words are motorcycle, car, truck, train, and subway. The words tire and wheel are not vehicles and are not correct.
6	-	The correct answers are: stove - kitchen, couch – living room, chest of drawers- bedroom, refrigerator- kitchen, sink- kitchen, dresser- bedroom, recliner- living room, bed- bedroom, and TV- living room. These are the only correct answers.
7	-	The only words that belong in the group of family members are Uncle, Cousin, Mother, Daughter, Son, Grandmother, Dad and Sister. The other words are not family member names and are not correct.
8	A	The correct answer is Mouth-watering, juicy, delicious, spicy.
9	-	The correct answers are Freddie and Jeremiah played tennis with their rackets. When a goal is made in soccer, the ball is kicked into the net. You use a bat in baseball. Touchdowns are made in football. These are the only correct answers.
10	A, B	The color words that have shades of the color in them are blue, sky blue, navy and red, scarlet, candy apple. The other words do not have shades of the color in them and are not correct.

Lesson 24: Shades of Word Meanings

Question No.	Answer	Detailed Explanations
1	B	The verbs that are similar (related) to each other and describe what you could do with a ball are - toss, drop, throw, hurl, pitch, bounce. That is the correct answer. The other list of verbs describes eating or drinking and is not correct.
2	-	The correct matches of verbs that are related or similar are tidy, clean to neat; weep, sob to cry; tired, drowsy to sleepy; chat, talk to speak. These are the only correct matches.
3	jump	The correct replacement for a related verb in the sentence is jump. It is the only verb that would make sense. We could not believe that he could jump so high in the air.
4	B	The correct answer is the second sentence. She giggled when she saw the funny face on the clown. The verb that is related to laugh in the sentence is giggled. The other sentences do not have related verbs and are not correct.
5	yelled	The correct answer is yelled as it is related to shouted. The angry man yelled at the kids when they walked on his grass. This is the only correct answer.
6	C	The third pair of verbs are NOT related- work, play. This is the correct answer. The other verbs- climb, go up- ran, sped- excited, thrilled are related and are not the correct answers.
7	-	The correct related adjectives to like adjectives are silly, funny to hilarious; thin, skinny to slender; pretty, gorgeous to beautiful; and fat, plump to overweight. These are the only correct answers.
8	C	The correct answer is the third answer- freezing, cold, frosty. The other answers are not correct as they could not describe the weather.
9	-	The correct answer is excellent as it is related to the adjective good. The boys did an excellent job on their project.
10	A, D	The correct 2 sentences that use adjectives related to the adjective-main are the first and fourth sentences. The important information is in the first paragraph. The major information is in the first paragraph. The second and third sentences do not have adjectives related to main and are not correct.

Lesson 25: Vocabulary Acquisition

Question No.	Answer	Detailed Explanations
1	-	The correct answers are deep, dark. They describe the woods in the story. They are the only correct answers.
2	-	The correct answers are frightened, scared. They tell about being afraid. They are the only correct answers.
3	C, D, E	The correct answers that tell how George and Timothy talked in the story are replied, said, shouted. These are the words used in the conversation and are the only correct answers. The other words answered and spoke are not found in the story. They are not correct.
4	-	-
5	C	The third sentence describes how the girls' parents feel- They are happy when they see the girls happy. This is the correct answer. The first, second and fourth sentences do not tell about how the parents feel. They are not correct.
6	D	The correct answer is the fourth sentence. He grins when he sees his sisters grinning at him as he finds more shells. The brother and the sisters are grinning. This is the only correct answer, as the first, second and third sentences do not have the same related action word in them for the sisters and brother.
7	A, E, F, G	The words that describe Hattie May are active adorable, energetic, friendly, typical gentle. The other words do not apply and are not correct.
8	B, C	The second and third sentences explain how Hattie May is obedient and intelligent. She comes to me when I call her, follows me wherever I go, and stays by me when we are outside. You can tell her basic commands and she knows what to do. The first and fourth sentences are not correct as they do not explain how she is obedient and intelligent.
9	A	The first sentence is the correct answer as it is NOT stated in the text. The other sentences are in the text and support the information.
10	-	The correct order of phrases in the sentence is- The lazy cat slept on the soft velvet couch in the sunny afternoon. This is the only correct answer.

Chapter 5 - Writing

The Writing standards for G-2 offer a focus for instruction to help ensure that students gain adequate mastery of a range of skills and applications. In their writing, students should demonstrate increasing sophistication in all aspects of language use, from vocabulary and syntax to the development and organization of ideas, and they should address increasingly demanding content and sources. Students advancing through the grades are expected to meet each year's grade-specific standards and retain or further develop skills and understandings mastered in preceding grades.

Name: ______________________ Date: ______________

Chapter 5

Lesson 1: Introducing and Closing Topics and connecting ideas

You can scan the QR code given below or use the url to access additional EdSearch resources including videos and mobile apps related to Introducing and Closing Topics and connecting ideas.

***edSearch* Introducing and Closing Topics and connecting ideas**

URL	QR Code
http://www.lumoslearning.com/a/w21	

Informative/Explanatory Writing

You read information about many things. When we write or read passages that tell or inform us, we call it informative, or explanatory writing. Your science and social studies books have this kind of writing.

Informative writing includes a topic sentence that tells what you are about to read.

Then important facts are given to tell you more. These facts give examples to support them.

At the end of the writing, there is a concluding statement that retells the topic sentence.

1. What does an informative/explanatory piece of writing tell you? Mark the best answer.

Ⓐ It gives you examples.
Ⓑ It has a topic sentence.
Ⓒ It has a conclusion.
Ⓓ It tells or informs you about things.

Read the information below and answer the question no 2, 3 & 4

<u>Spring</u>

We see weather changes along with new animal and plant life in the Spring.
Spring is a season that comes after winter and before summer. The weather is not as cold as in winter. The sun rises earlier in the morning and sets later in the afternoon during Spring. The months when Spring occurs in the U.S. are March through May.
Flowers bloom in Spring and trees have new leaves. Many people grow flowers and vegetables during this season.
Animals also have babies during Spring. Birds and rabbits can be seen more outside.

2. Which is the topic sentence in the writing?

Ⓐ The months when Spring occurs in the U.S. are March through May.
Ⓑ We see weather changes along with new animal and plant life in the Spring.
Ⓒ Many people grow flowers and vegetables during this season.
Ⓓ Flowers bloom in Spring and trees have new leaves.

3. What are the 3 facts that are used in the writing about Spring?

Ⓐ Animals have babies
Ⓑ School is out
Ⓒ Dogs bark
Ⓓ Flowers bloom and leaves grow
Ⓔ Weather is cooler

4. The writing does not have a concluding statement. Choose the sentence that would best help to end this writing about Spring.

Ⓐ Spring has weather changes.
Ⓑ Leaves come out.
Ⓒ Baby birds are born
Ⓓ Spring brings cooler weather and new life for animals and plants.

Read the information below and answer the question no 5, 6 & 7

We love to read stories about things that have happened or make-believe.
These stories are called narratives. They have a setting (time and place where the story happened), characters (people or animals in the story), a story theme (problem, solution and sequence of events), and an ending or closure to the story.
Good narratives use descriptive words to make you want to read more. They also contain words that show the order of events (examples- first, next, then, last, finally, when, then, before, after, also). Some narratives have conversation in them, too.
Read the question and answer them to make your narrative story about going on a trip.

5. Your friend, Harry, and you are going on a camping trip. Which sentence would be the best to begin your story?
(Remember that description words are the best to use in writing.) Mark your answer.

Ⓐ Harry and I are going camping.
Ⓑ Harry and I are excited to go camping in the Rocky Mountains.
Ⓒ Harry and I are going somewhere.
Ⓓ Harry and I are going on a trip.

6. Read the sentences below. They are not in the correct order to make sense in a story about Harry and you going camping. Write them in the correct order to make sense.

Ⓐ First, we got our camping gear ready and packed it in the van. We packed plenty of food and water, a sturdy tent, sleeping bags, clothes for hiking, fishing poles, and a lantern to see at night.
Ⓑ Harry and I are ready to go again!
Ⓒ We stayed for two nights and had so much fun hiking and fishing.
Ⓓ When we set up our tent, Harry exclaimed, "Wow! Look how gorgeous the mountains are! I am so happy we are here!"
Ⓔ Harry and I are excited to go camping in the Rocky Mountains.
Ⓕ Then, Dad drove us to the camp site and dropped us off.

7. Words can help to show sequence of events in a story. Mark the words in the box if they do or do not show sequence.

	Shows sequence	Does not show sequence
then		
room		
first		
before		
saw		

8. Your class took a trip to the zoo. Using the following words, write 2 sentences that show what you might have seen. You need to have descriptive words in each sentence you write. Remember that a descriptive word can be an adjective that you use to help you describe a noun (name) of something.

elephant
monkey

9. Begin with a topic sentence. Fill in the blank below to get started.

My favorite food is ______________________.

9.1 Now using your topic sentence, think of why you like this kind of food. List 3 reasons.

9.3 Rewrite the topic sentence to make it a conclusion. Say the same thing but change the words.

10.Read the opinion paragraph about pets and answer the question.

My favorite pet is a dog. I like dogs because they are loving, play with you, and can be taught tricks. Dogs like to be petted and like to sleep by you. They can run with you and fetch balls. You can teach a dog to fetch, roll over, beg, and play dead. Dogs are the best pets ever.

Which sentence is the conclusion in the paragraph? Write the sentence.

Name: ______________________ Date: ______________

Chapter 4

Lesson 2: Produce, publish and research

You can scan the QR code given below or use the url to access additional EdSearch resources including videos and mobile apps related to Produce, publish and research

Produce, publish and research

URL	QR Code
http://www.lumoslearning.com/a/w26	

Name: ______________________ Date: ______________

When you read or write a story, it is important to use capital letters at the beginning of each sentence and when using proper nouns. We call it editing and revising when we make changes and corrections to writing.

It is also important to punctuate your sentences when writing. Periods are used at the end of sentences, question marks for asking questions, and exclamation marks for sentences that show excitement.

Ask your teacher for help if you need to.

1. Read the sentences below. Rewrite and edit them making corrections to capitalization.

1. he did not understand what maria was saying in spanish.

2. they wanted to go to disneyworld.

2. Read the sentences below. Rewrite and edit them making corrections to punctuation.

1. May I have a glass of water

2. We went downtown with Uncle Fred

Name: ______________________ Date: ______________

3. **Read the selection below and rewrite by editing capitalization and punctuation.**

he was going to the store aunt beth asked him to get a loaf of bread and milk tom rode his bike there

4. **Sometimes when you read a story, it may not make sense. There might be something in the story that does not belong. Revising the story and leaving that part out makes it better.**

Read the selection below and highlight the sentence that does NOT belong in the story.

Amanda and her brother needed to clean their rooms. It was a chore they did not like but had to do every week. Mom baked a cake. Today they happily got to work. Their dad promised to take them to the lake to go fishing when they were finished. It did not take them long to get their rooms tidy. Dad was pleased and off they went!

5. **You teacher assigned you to write a paper. The paper must have online research (facts and information to share) to support it.**

Read the list of topics below. Mark the ones that would follow the assignment. Remember that you must have facts from sources online.

Ⓐ How to grow vegetables
Ⓑ What makes me laugh
Ⓒ My brother is silly
Ⓓ Fantastic Bugs
Ⓔ All about zoo animals
Ⓕ If food could talk
Ⓖ Facts about the US

6. You have to interview a weather man (meteorologist) and share what you learn with the class.

The words below were given to you by your teacher to learn before the interview. Read the words and decide which digital tools could help you. Mark the digital tool answers.

Anemometer
Rain gauge
Weather vane
Thermometer
Radar

Ⓐ Online dictionary
Ⓑ Online encyclopedia
Ⓒ Web search for meteorologist

7. It is important that you have someone review your work when you write. Your teacher can do this and so can other classmates. It is called "peer collaboration" when your classmates or friends help you to review, revise, and edit your writing.

Read the selection below that a fellow classmate might have written. If you were doing a "peer collaboration", what suggestions might you give your classmate to help him improve on his writing? Mark the ones that would help.

I am going to learn how to surf with my uncle jeff. He has been a surfer for many years. uncle jeff won first place last year in the San Diego Surf Contest it was his second year to win. How fantastic now he's ready to teach me his secrets

Ⓐ Check capitalization for beginning of sentences and proper nouns.
Ⓑ Leave out the first sentence as it does not make sense.
Ⓒ Check for punctuation, as many periods and an exclamation point are missing.
Ⓓ It does not need revising or editing.

8. You have written about a topic, putting microchips in pets. You ask your teacher for help in reviewing your work. You are most concerned about how current your information is that you found. Which years would NOT show current information? Mark your answers.

Ⓐ 2018
Ⓑ 2017
Ⓒ 2001
Ⓓ 1988

Name: ______________________ Date: ______________

About the invention of the wheel

Read the three articles below and answer the questions. The following information is about 3 types of important inventions.

#1 - About the invention of the wheel-

No one knows who invented the wheel. It was over thousands of years ago that it was first used. We read about chariots and carts which had wheels attached to them.

Wheels can be found on other things, too. Water can be moved by wheels on power mills and pulleys.

Now we still rely on wheels to help us with transportation, engines, motors, jets, power plants, and in tools for scientific research.

#2-About the invention of the plow-

The plow was even used in what is called "prehistoric" times. Before the plow, people did not grow their own food, they lived by searching for food.

The plow makes work easier for farmers. It was improved upon and now people can grow and harvest more food than they need. This started the trading industry for farmers.

#3- About the invention of the printing press-

The printing press was invented by Johann Gutenberg in the 1430s. He put together the idea of block printing with a screw press. Then he made metal printing blocks for letters that were better than the previous wooden ones. He also improved the ink and paper process to make multiple copies of papers.

He helped people make books and newspapers cheaper. This made information easier to record and share around the world.

9. In which ways do wheels help us now? List them.

10. **What did the plow help start for the farmers?**

End of Writing

Answer Key and Detailed Explanations

Chapter 5: Writing

Lesson 1: Introducing and Closing Topics and connecting ideas

Question No.	Answer	Detailed Explanations
1	D	-
2	B	The topic sentence in the writing is- We see weather changes along with new plant and animal life in the Spring. This sentence tells what the writing will be about. The other sentences give details but do not tell the most and are not correct.
3	A, D, E	The correct answer for facts in the writing about Spring are- animals have babies, flowers bloom and leaves grow, and weather is cooler. The other details are not found and are not correct.
4	D	The best concluding statement for the writing is- Spring brings cooler weather and new life for animals and plants.
5	B	The best answer is- Harry and I are excited to go camping in the Rocky Mountains. This sentence uses descriptive words and gets the reader's attention. It is correct. The other sentences do not use descriptive words and are not the best. They are not correct.
6	-	The correct story sequence is- Harry and I are excited to go camping in the Rocky Mountains. First, we got our camping gear ready and packed it in the van. We packed plenty of food and water, a sturdy tent, sleeping bags, clothes for hiking, fishing poles, and a lantern to see at night. Then, Dad drove us to the camp site and dropped us off. When we set up our tent, Harry exclaimed, "Wow! Look how gorgeous the mountains are! I am so happy we are here!" We stayed for two nights and had so much fun hiking and fishing. Harry and I are ready to go again! This is the only correct story sequence that makes sense.
7	-	The words that should be marked to show sequence are – then, first, before. The words that should be marked that do not show sequence are room and saw. These are the only correct answers.

Question No.	Answer	Detailed Explanations
8	-	Answers will vary but must include a descriptive word for elephant and a descriptive word for monkey. The answers must also relate to being at the zoo and be in complete sentences.
9	-	Answers will vary. All food types are acceptable and correct. My favorite food is____________.
9.1	-	Answers will vary. Be sure that the answers match why they like the food they chose.
9.2	-	Answers will vary but must be the same focus as the topic sentence the students wrote.
10	-	The correct answer is- Dogs are the best pets ever. This sentence is the conclusion sentence and can be found at the end of the paragraph.

Lesson 2: Produce, publish and research

Question No.	Answer	Detailed Explanations
1	-	The correct editing should be 1. He did not understand what Maria was saying in Spanish. 2. They wanted to go to Disneyworld.
2	-	1. May I have a glass of water? 2. We went downtown with Uncle Fred.
3	-	The correct editing of the selection is- He was going to the store. Aunt Beth asked him to get a loaf of bread and milk. Tom rode his bike there. This is the only correct answer.
4	-	The sentence that does NOT belong in the selection is- Mom baked a cake. It does not belong because it has nothing to do with them cleaning their rooms and why they were happy to do it today. It is the only correct answer.
5	A, D, E, G	The correct answers that would be supported in online research are- How to grow vegetables, Fantastic Bugs, All about zoo animals and Facts about the US. The other topics do relate to factual information and would not require online digital research. They are not correct.
6	A, B, C	All of the digital tools listed would help you before you interview the meteorologist. Online dictionary, Online encyclopedia, and Web search for meteorologist.
7	A, C	The suggestions that you might share in "peer collaboration" are the first and third sentences. Check capitalization for beginning of sentences and proper nouns. Check for punctuation, as many periods and an exclamation point are missing. They are correct. The second and fourth sentences are not correct.
8	C, D	The years that would not show current information are 2001, and 1988, as these are over 15+ years old and considered out-of-date. These are the correct answers.
9	-	The correct answers are transportation, engines, motors, jets, power plants, and tools for scientific research. These are the only correct answers found in the article.
10	-	The only answer is – the trading industry. No other answers are correct.

Additional Information

Why Practice with Repeated Reading Passages?

Throughout the Lumos Learning Common Core Practice workbooks, students and educators will notice many passages repeat. This is done intentionally. The goal of these workbooks is to help students practice skills necessary to be successful in class and on standardized tests. One of the most critical components to that success is the ability to read and comprehend passages. To that end, reading fluency must be strengthened. According to Hasbrouck and Tindal (2006), "Helping our students become fluent readers is absolutely critical for proficient and motivated reading" (p. 642). And, Nichols et al. indicate, (2009), "fluency is a gateway to comprehension that enables students to move from being word decoders to passage comprehenders" (p. 11).

Lumos Learning recognizes there is no one-size-fits-all approach to build fluency in readers; however, the repeated reading of passages, where students read the same passages at least two or more times, is one of the most widely recognized strategies to improve fluency (Nichols et al., 2009). Repeated reading allows students the opportunity to read passages with familiar words several times until the passage becomes familiar and they no longer have to decode word by word. As students reread, the decoding barrier falls away allowing for an increase in reading comprehension.

The goal of the Lumos Learning workbooks is to increase student achievement and preparation for any standardized test. Using some passages multiple times in a book offers struggling readers an opportunity to do just that.

References

Hasbrouck, J., and Tindal, G. (2006). Oral reading fluency norms: A valuable assessment tool for reading teachers. Reading Teacher, 59(7), 636644. doi:10.1598/RT.59.7.3. Nichols, W., Rupley, W., and Rasinski, T. (2009). Fluency in learning to read for meaning: going beyond repeated readings. Literacy Research & Instruction, 48(1). doi:10.1080/19388070802161906.

What if I buy more than one Lumos Study Program?

Step 1

Visit the URL and login to your account.
http://www.lumoslearning.com

Step 2

Click on 'My tedBooks' under the "Account" tab.
Place the Book Access Code and submit.

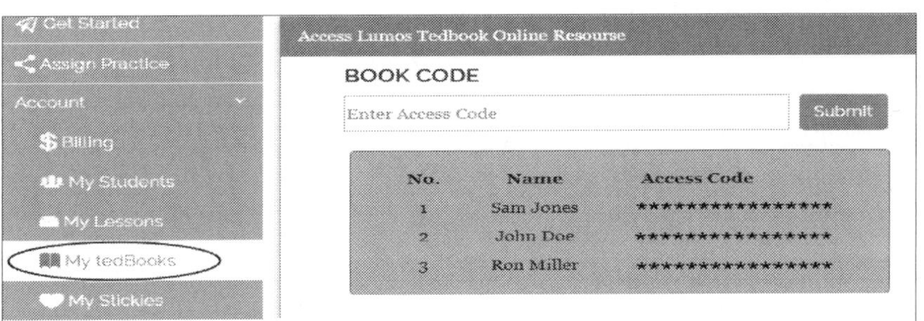

Step 3

To add the new book for a registered student, choose the Existing Student button and select the student and submit.

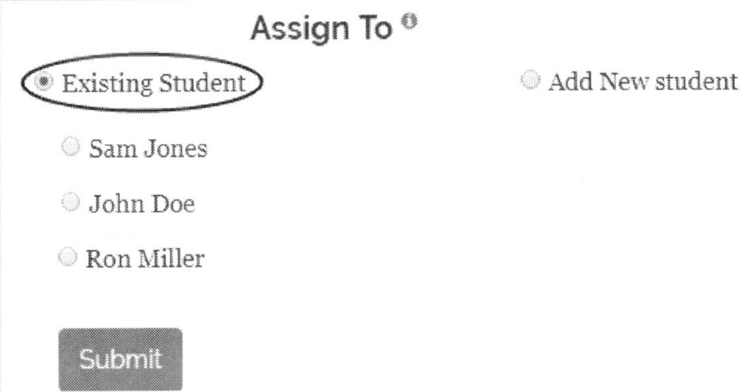

To add the new book for a new student, choose the Add New student button and complete the student registration.

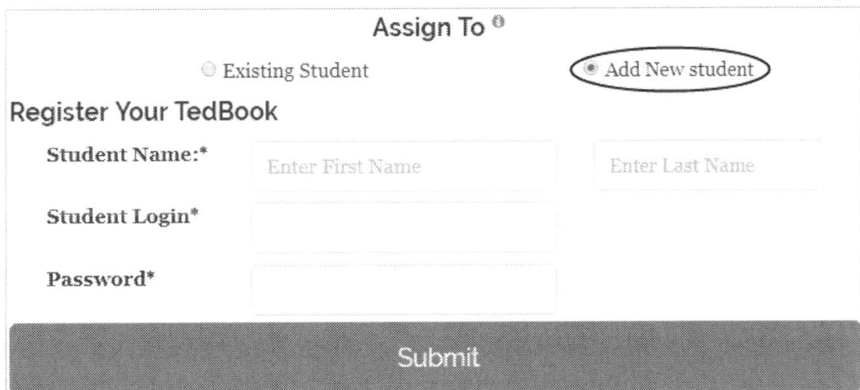

Lumos StepUp® Mobile App FAQ For Students

What is the Lumos StepUp® App?

It is a FREE application you can download onto your Android Smartphones, tablets, iPhones, and iPads.

What are the Benefits of the StepUp® App?

This mobile application gives convenient access to Practice Tests, Common Core State Standards, Online Workbooks, and learning resources through your Smartphone and tablet computers.

- Eleven Technology enhanced question types in both MATH and ELA
- Sample questions for Arithmetic drills
- Standard specific sample questions
- Instant access to the Common Core State Standards
- Jokes and cartoons to make learning fun!

Do I Need the StepUp® App to Access Online Workbooks?

No, you can access Lumos StepUp® Online Workbooks through a personal computer. The StepUp® app simply enhances your learning experience and allows you to conveniently access StepUp® Online Workbooks and additional resources through your smart phone or tablet.

How can I Download the App?

Visit **lumoslearning.com/a/stepup-app** using your Smartphone or tablet and follow the instructions to download the app.

QR Code for Smartphone Or Tablet Users

Lumos StepUp® Mobile App FAQ For Parents and Teachers

What is the Lumos StepUp® App?

It is a free app that teachers can use to easily access real-time student activity information as well as assign learning resources to students. Parents can also use it to easily access school-related information such as homework assigned by teachers and PTA meetings. It can be downloaded onto Smartphones and tablets from popular App Stores.

What are the Benefits of the Lumos StepUp® App?

It provides convenient access to

- Standards aligned learning resources for your students
- An easy to use Dashboard
- Student progress reports
- Active and inactive students in your classroom
- Professional development information
- Educational Blogs

How can I Download the App?

Visit **lumoslearning.com/a/stepup-app** using your Smartphone or tablet and follow the instructions provided to download the App.

QR Code
for Smartphone
Or Tablet Users

Progress Chart

Standard	Lesson	Page No.	Practice		Mastered	Re-practice /Reteach
CCSS			Date	Score		
RL.2.1	The Question Session	6				
RL.2.2	Recount stories	12				
RL.2.3	Describing Characters	17				
RL.2.4	Figurative Language	22				
RL.2.5	How is it Written?	26				
RL.2.6	Point of View	32				
RL.2.7	I Can See It!	37				
RL.2.9	Alike and Different	44				
RI.2.1	Ask and answer questions	62				
RI.2.2	The Main idea	67				
RI.2.3	Connect the dots	73				
RI.2.4	What Does It Mean?	78				
RI.2.5	Special Text Parts	82				
RI.2.6	The main purpose of a text	88				
RI.2.7	Informational Illustrations	93				
RI.2.8	Reason it out	100				
RI.2.9	Compare and contrast	105				
RF.2.3	Decode the words	123				
RF.2.4	Comprehend the text	127				
RF.2.4A	Understand the purpose of the text	131				
RF.2.4C	Use context to find the meaning of words	136				

Standard	Lesson	Page No.	Practice		Mastered	Re-practice /Reteach
CCSS			Date	Score		
L.2.1A	People, Places, and Things	147				
L.1.2	Language conventions	151				
L.2.1B	Regular and Irregular Plural Nouns.	156				
L.2.1C	Reflective pronouns	161				
L.2.1D	Past tense of verbs	165				
L.2.1F	Simple and compound sentences	169				
L.2.2	Understand Language conventions.	174				
L.2.2A	How is it Capitalized?	179				
L.2.2B	The Comma and Quotation Dilemma	183				
L.2.2C	Use an apostrophe	188				
L.2.2D	Spelling patterns	192				
L.2.2E	Consult reference materials	197				
L.2.3	Use knowledge of language and its conventions	202				
L.2.3A	Formal and Informal language	206				
L.2.4	Same Word Different Meanings	211				
L.2.4B	Prefix and Suffix	215				
L.2.1E	Adjective and Adverb	219				
L.2.4A	The context clue	223				
L.2.4C	Roots and affixes	228				
L.2.4D	Connecting related words	233				
L.2.4E	Find the meaning	238				
L.2.5	The meaning of words	243				
L.2.5A	Usage of words	248				
L.2.5.B	Shades of word meaning	254				
L.2.6	Vocabulary acquisition	258				
W.2.1	Introducing and Closing Topics and connecting ideas	292				
W.2.6	Produce, publish and research	298				

Made in United States
Orlando, FL
27 September 2022